1p, 2p and 5p coins

1

How much?

 Alice has 2p

 John has ☐

 Kim has ☐

 Alan has ☐

 Gavin has ☐

 Pam has ☐

 Janis has ☐

 Tessa has ☐

Problem solving

Who can buy the 🍬 ?

Match the coins.

Money to 9p

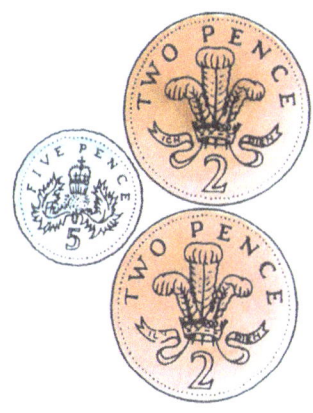

Problem solving

Colour **3** coins to buy a 🍬.

Ten pence

10p coin

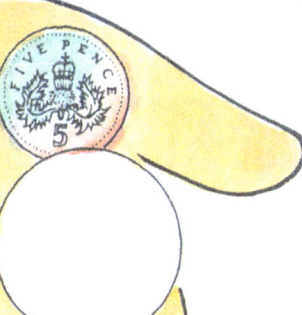
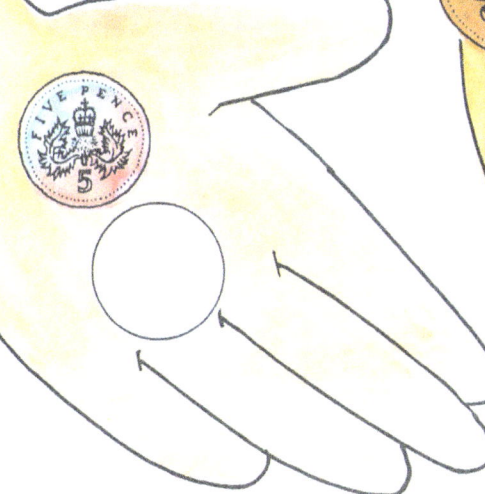

**Put out coins.
Make each set worth**

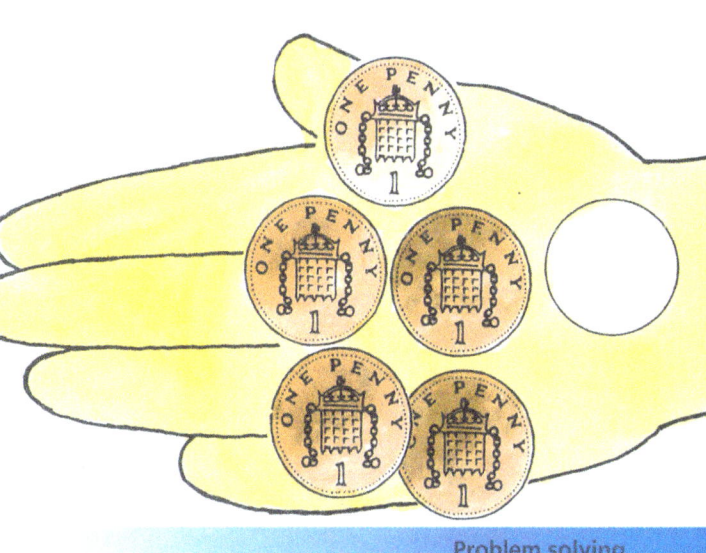

Problem solving

Colour coins to make 10p.

Problem solving

Buying things

Tom spends 10p altogether.
Write the price of the boat.

3p   2p

Lili spends 10p.
She buys two things.
Colour their labels.

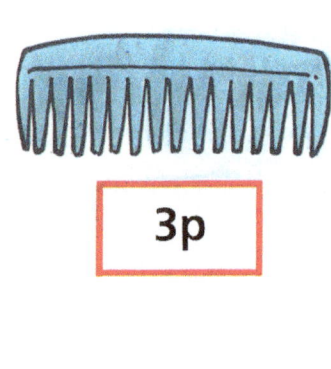

3p

6p

4p

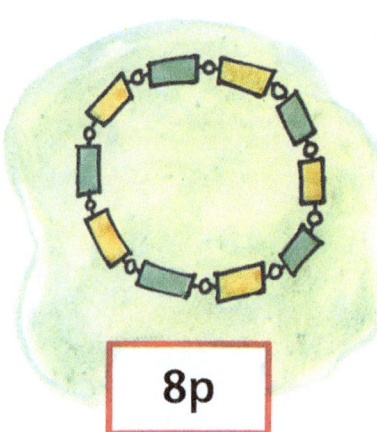

8p

7p

Buying stickers

Use coins. Put out the change.

Change from 5p

Change from 5p

Change from 10p

Change from 10p

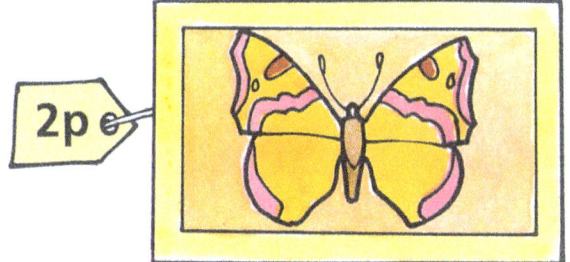

Change from 10p

show

Numbers to 20

Write the number

after 13

after 19

after 17

before 17

before 11

before 20

Counting to 20

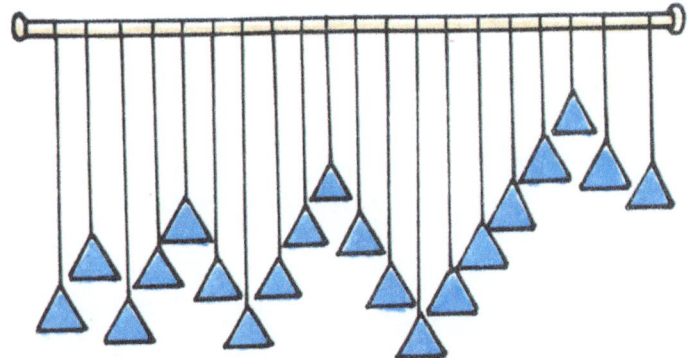

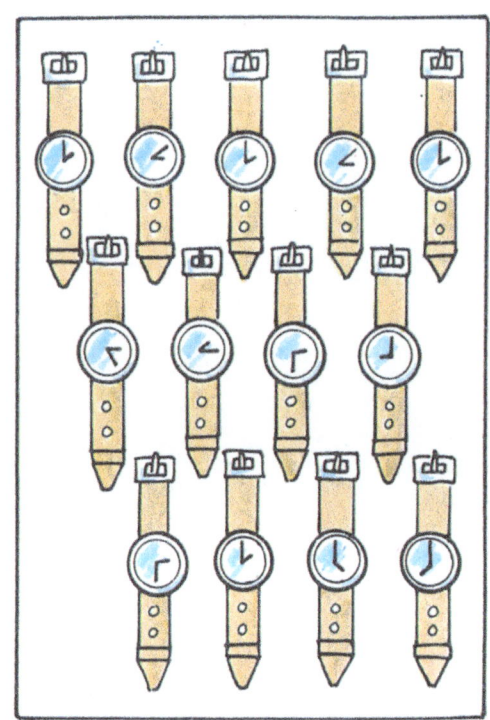

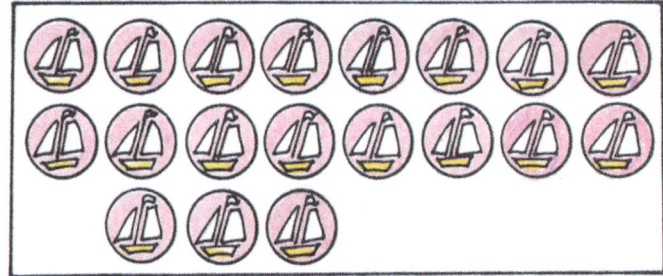

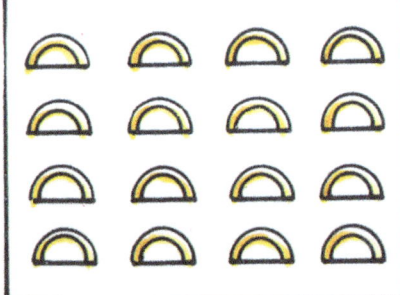
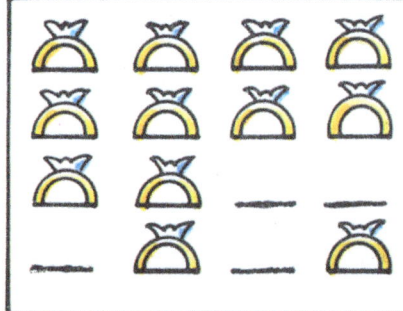

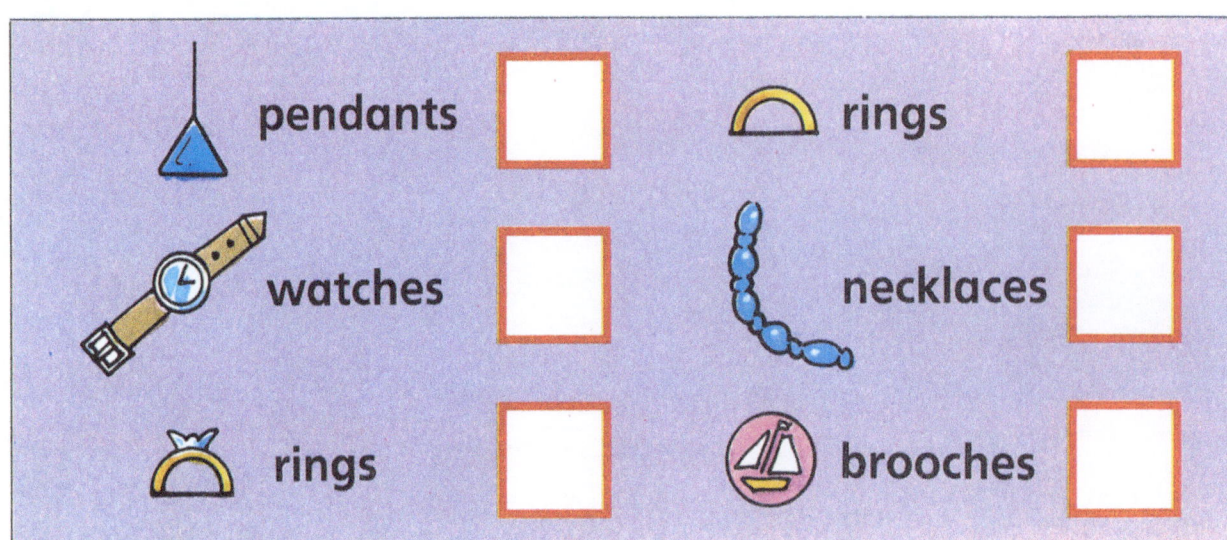

Jewellery shop

Counting to 20

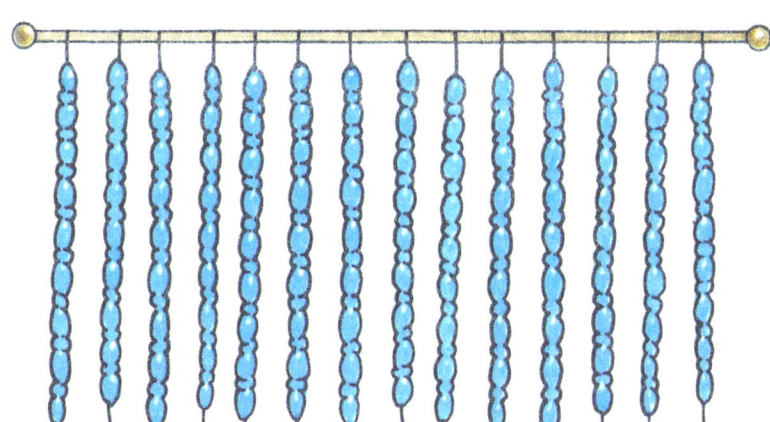
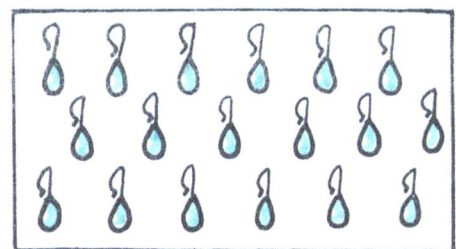

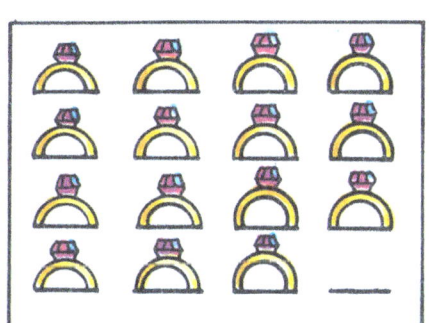
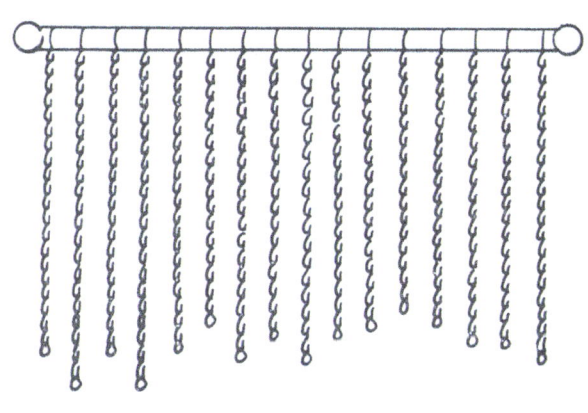
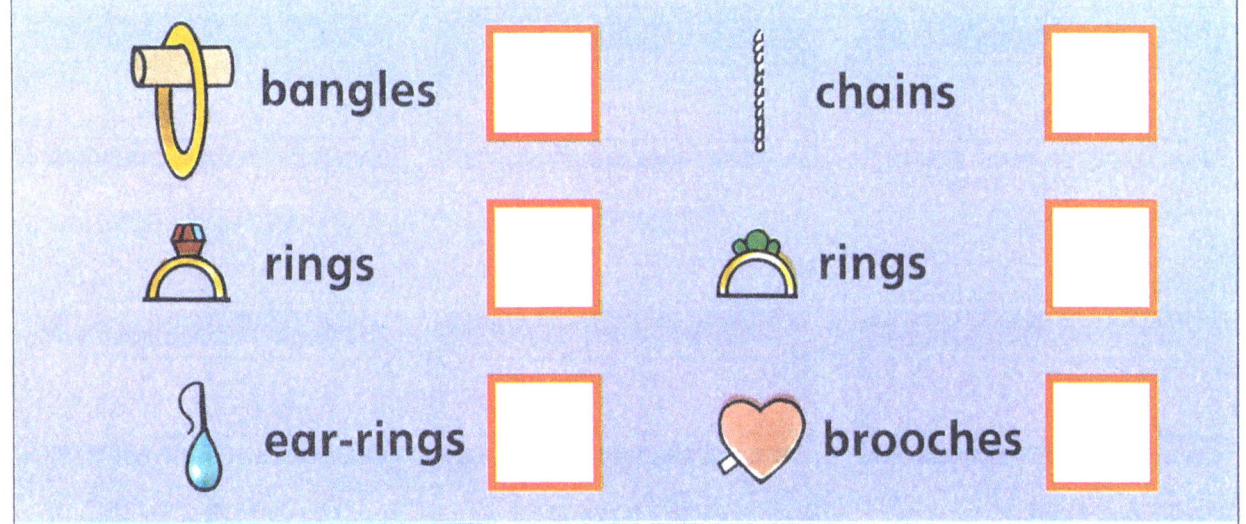

Number names to 20

Write the numbers.

Colour twenty red, twelve blue, thirteen yellow and

Use a calculator to show these numbers.
Write the numbers.

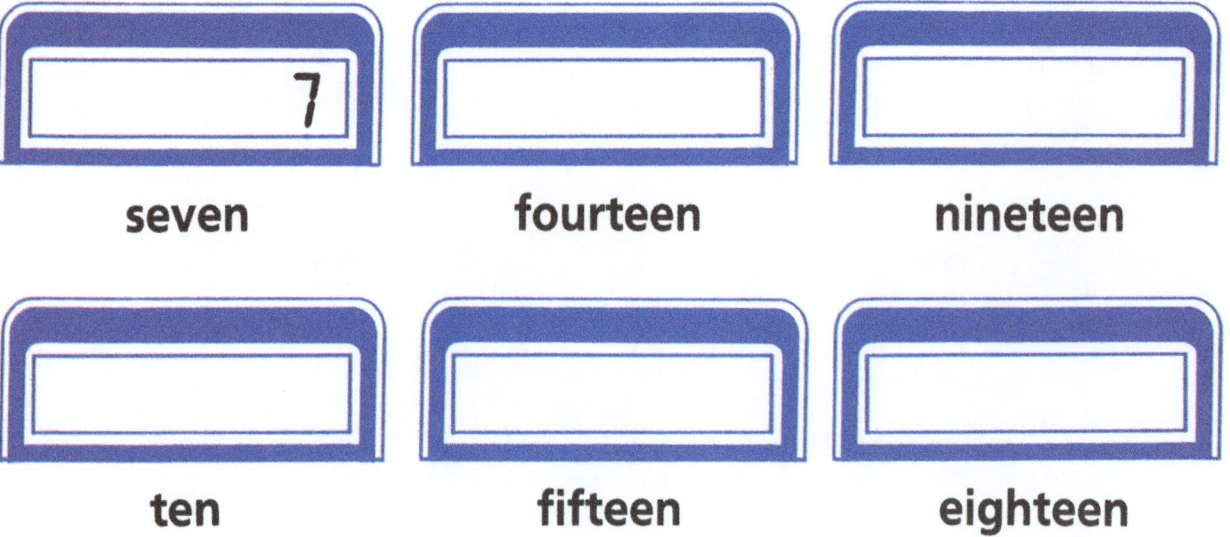

seven   fourteen   nineteen

ten   fifteen   eighteen

names

Number names to 20

12

sixteen   seventeen   eighteen   nineteen   twenty

seventeen green.

Match

nine
eleven
fourteen
sixteen

Towards place value

The sunflower

Use cubes.

Count out 13.
Put 10 on the  .
13 = 10 and 3

Count out 19.
Put 10 on the   .
19 = 10 and ___

Count out 15.
Put 10 on the   .
15 = 10 and ___

Count out 18.
Put 10 on the  .
18 = 10 and ___

Count out 16.
Put 10 on the   .
16 = ___ and ___

Count out 12.
Put 10 on the   .
12 = ___ and ___

The beanstalk

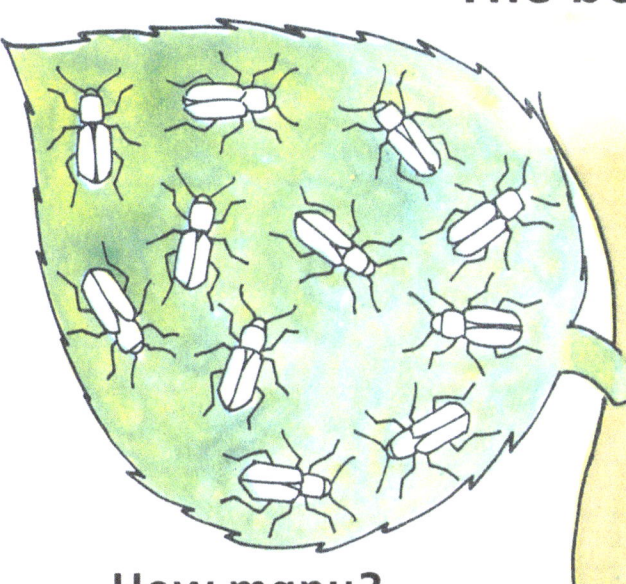

How many? ____
Colour 10 red.

11 = 10 + ____

How many? ____
Colour 10 yellow.

14 = 10 + ____

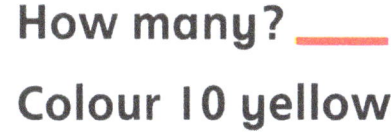

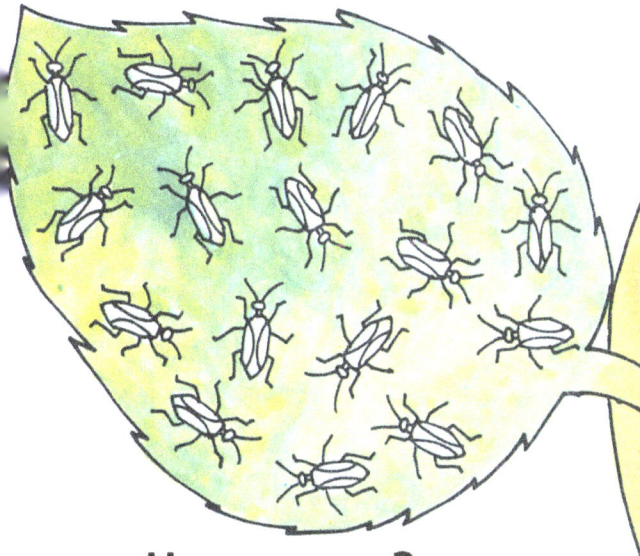

How many? ____
Colour 10 blue.

17 = ____ + ____

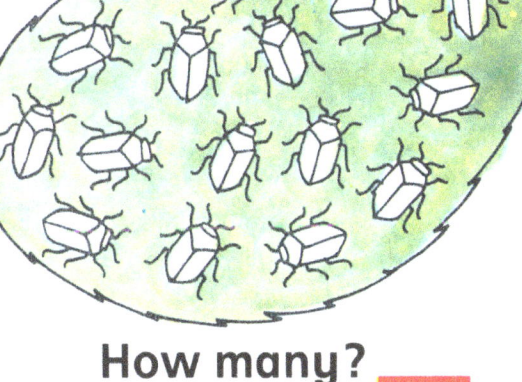

How many? ____
Colour 10 purple.

15 = ____ + ____

19 = ____ + ____
12 = ____ + ____
16 = ____ + ____

The garden centre

10 + ___

How many altogether?

10 + ___

How many altogether?

10 + ___

How many altogether?

10 + ___

How many altogether?

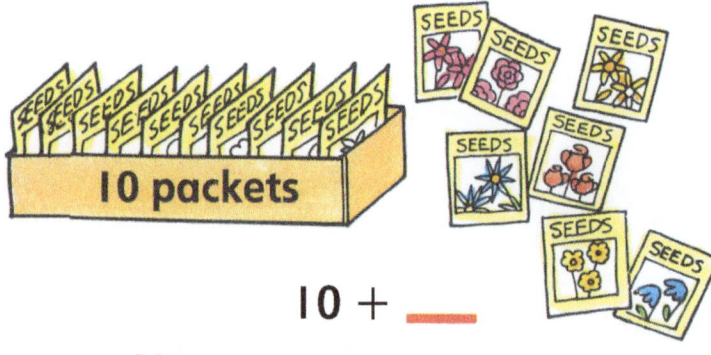

10 + ___

How many altogether?

10 + ___

How many altogether?

Loading bricks

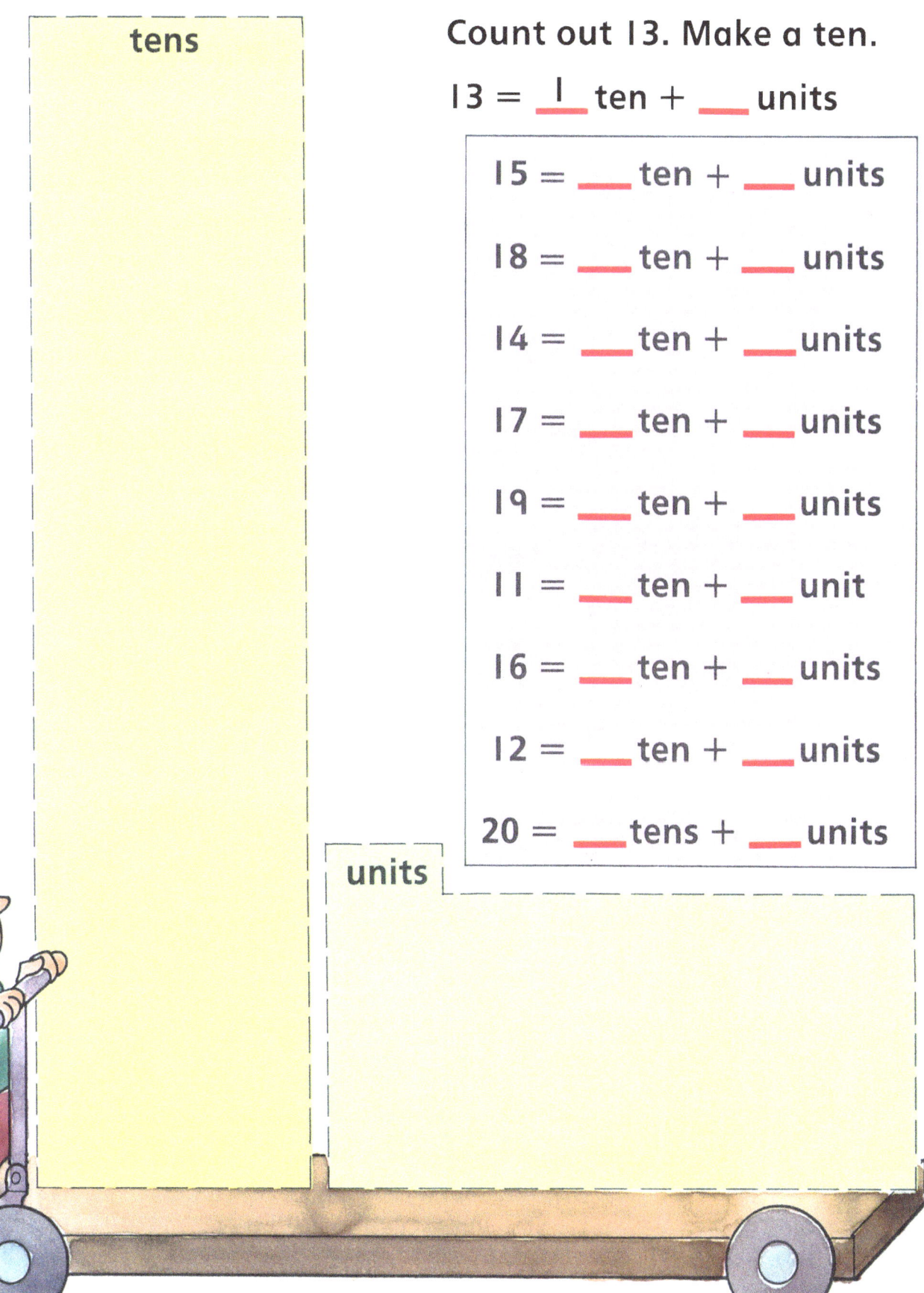

Count out 13. Make a ten.

13 = __1__ ten + ____ units

15 = ____ ten + ____ units

18 = ____ ten + ____ units

14 = ____ ten + ____ units

17 = ____ ten + ____ units

19 = ____ ten + ____ units

11 = ____ ten + ____ unit

16 = ____ ten + ____ units

12 = ____ ten + ____ units

20 = ____ tens + ____ units

Place value to 20

More bricks

tens

Put out 1 ten and 5 units.
How many cubes altogether? ☐

1 ten + 5 units = ☐

1 ten + 2 units = ☐

1 ten + 7 units = ☐

1 ten + 4 units = ☐

1 ten + 1 unit = ☐

1 ten + 6 units = ☐

2 tens + 0 units = ☐

units

Place value to 20

18

Cranes

Colour the boxes to match the cranes.

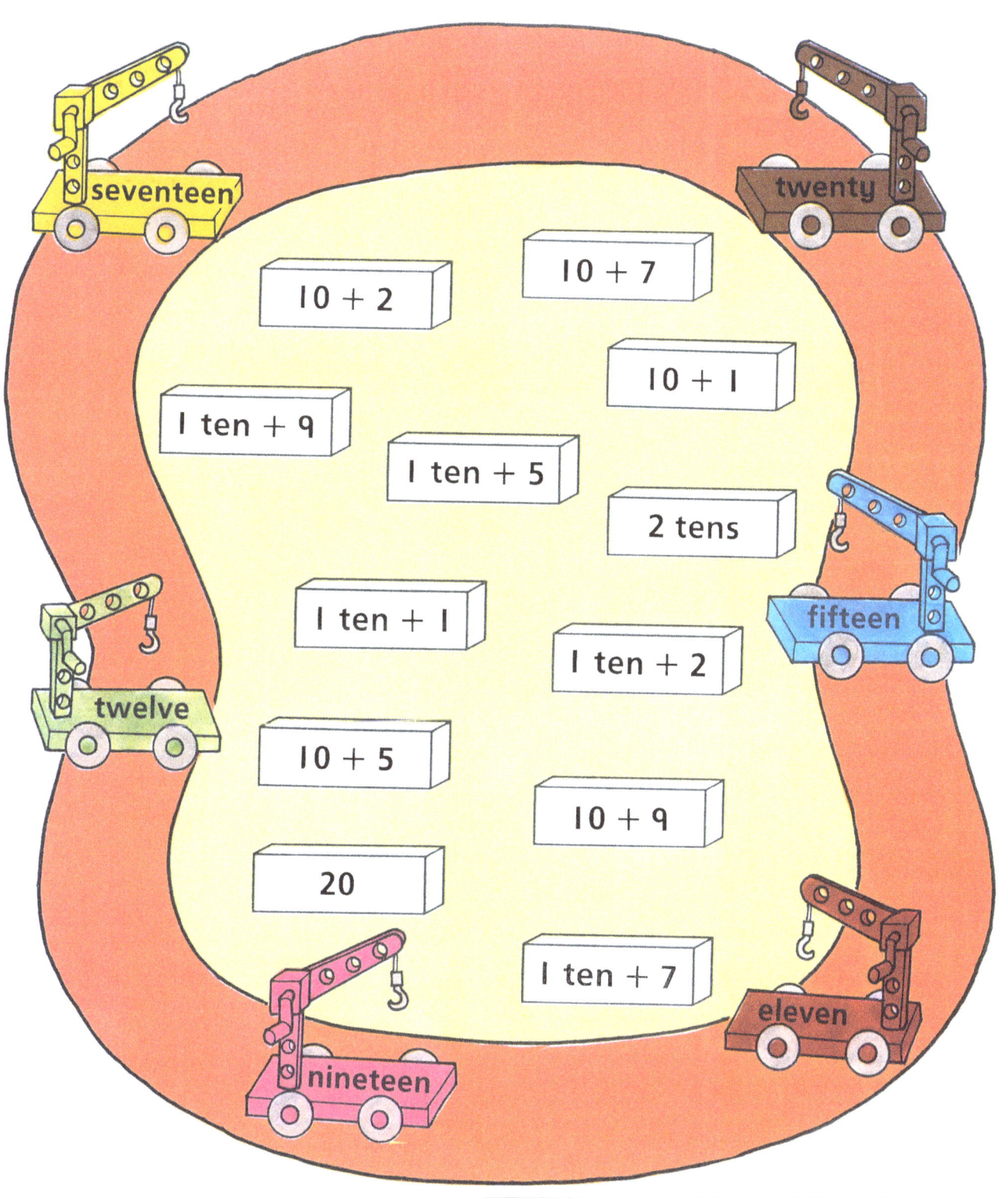

CARDS Place value to 20 Cards 1 to 6

Number line: counting on

Bunny hops

Start at 4.   Count on 3.   4 + 3 = ☐

Start at 8.   Count on 3.   8 + 3 = ☐

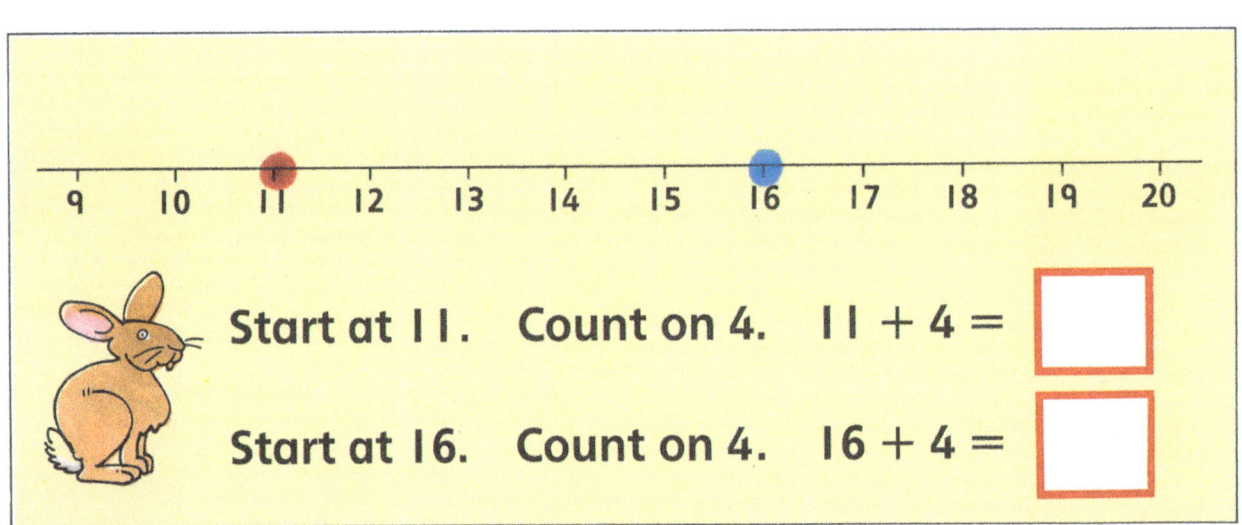

Start at 11.   Count on 4.   11 + 4 = ☐

Start at 16.   Count on 4.   16 + 4 = ☐

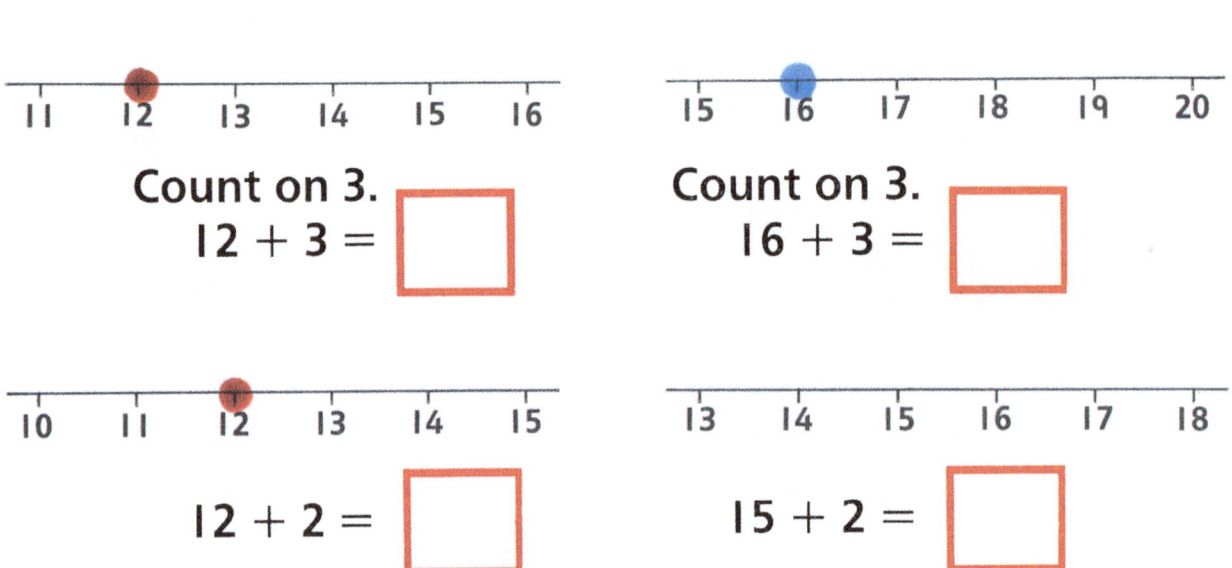

Count on 3.
12 + 3 = ☐

Count on 3.
16 + 3 = ☐

12 + 2 = ☐

15 + 2 = ☐

Party food

Put more cherries on the cake.

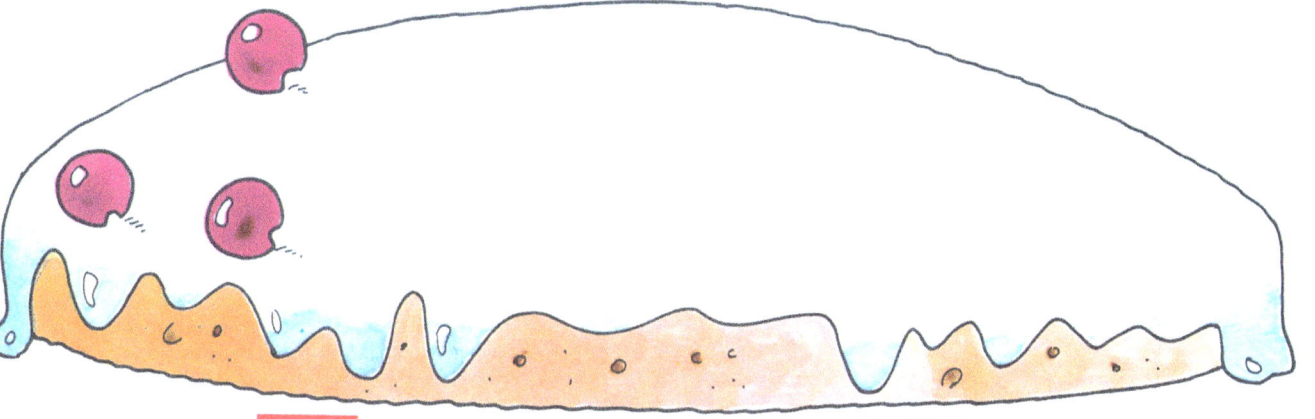

3 + ☐ = 5   3 + ☐ = 4

3 + ☐ = 6   3 + ☐ = 7

3 + ☐ = 9   3 + ☐ = 8

Draw more cakes.   Draw more cakes.

2 + ☐ = 5   5 + ☐ = 8

Draw more apples.   Draw more apples.

 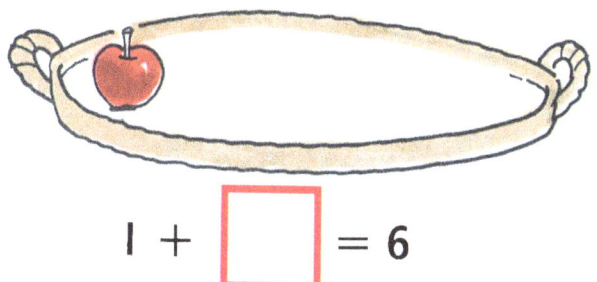

4 + ☐ = 7   1 + ☐ = 6

Boats

Vegetables

The difference in price is ☐ p.   6 − 4 =

You may use 🪙 coins.

  Difference in price ☐ p   8 − 2 =

  Difference in price ☐ p   9 − 6 =

  Difference in price ☐ p

 Difference in price ☐ p

 Difference in price ☐ p

Plants

☐ plants

☐ plants

The difference between 9 and 6 is ___ .   9 − 6 = ☐

☐ trees

☐ trees

The difference between 4 and 8 is ___ .   8 − 4 = ☐

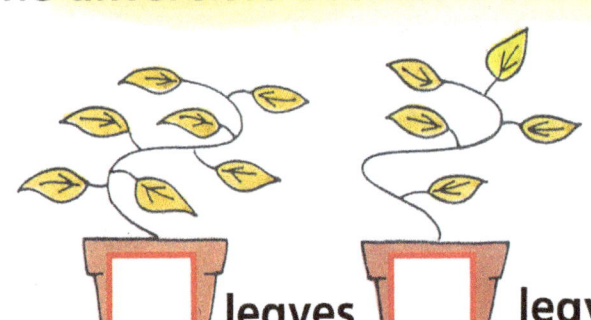

☐ leaves ☐ leaves

The difference between 7 and 5 is ___ .

7 − 5 = ☐

The difference between 6 and 3 is ___ .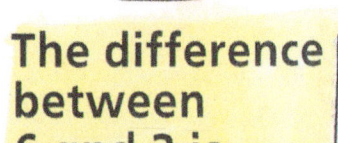

6 − 3 = ☐

 The difference between 2 and 9 is ___ .

9 − 2 = ☐

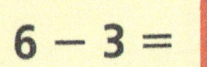

Money to 9p

2

Match the coins.

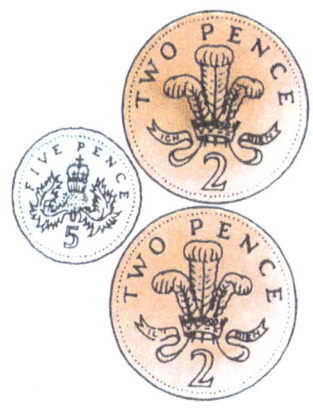

Problem solving

Colour 3 coins to buy a TOFFS.

Ten pence

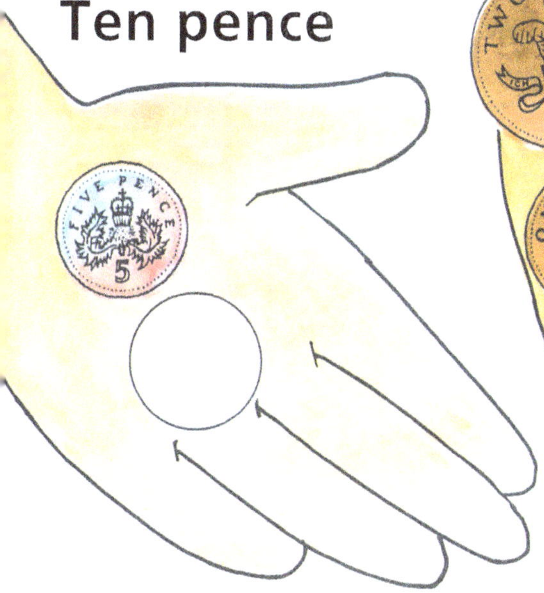

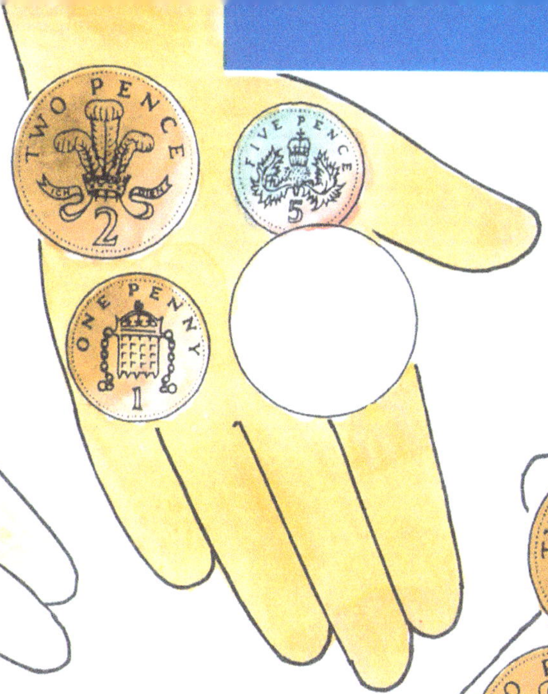

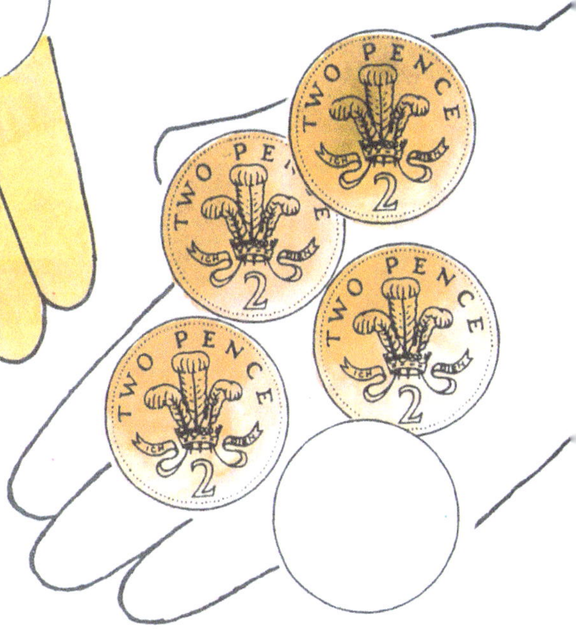

**Put out coins.
Make each set worth**

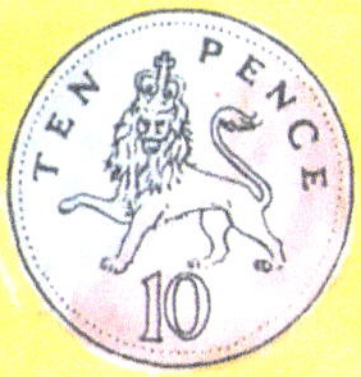

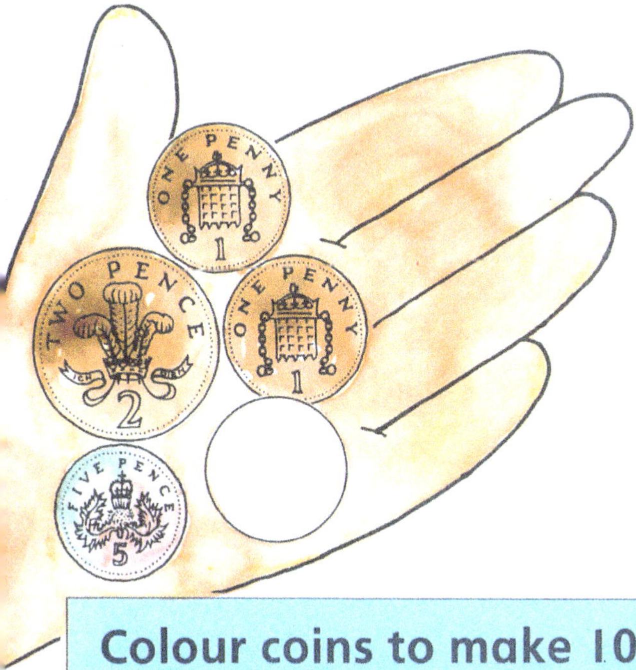

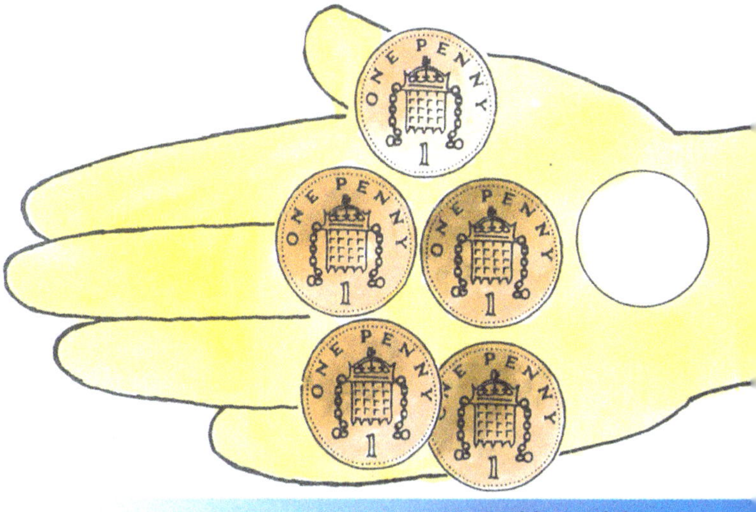

Problem solving

Colour coins to make 10p.

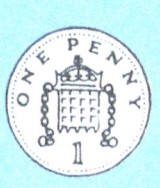

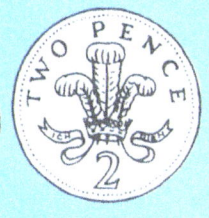

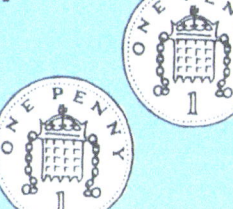

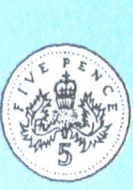

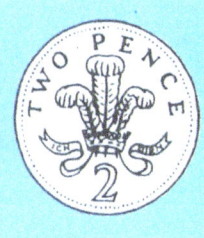

Problem solving

Buying things

Tom spends 10p altogether.
Write the price of the boat.

3p   2p

Lili spends 10p.
She buys two things.
Colour their labels.

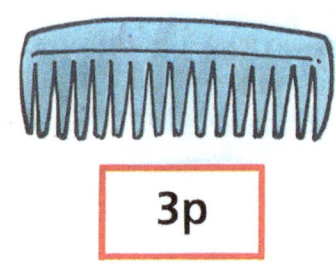
3p

6p

4p

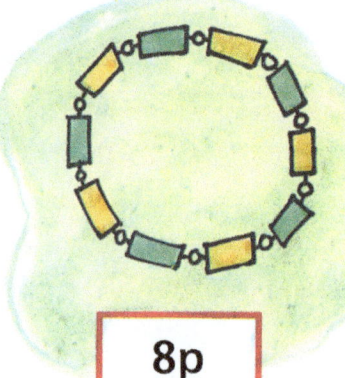
8p

7p

Buying stickers

Use coins. Put out the change.

Change from 5p

Change from 5p

Change from 10p

Change from 10p

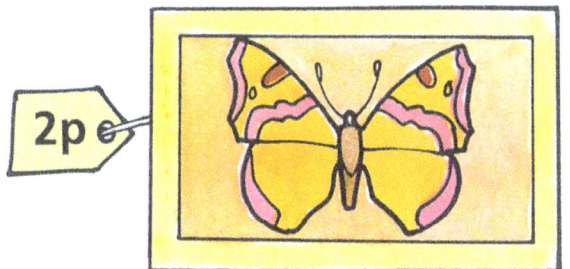

Change from 10p

show

Numbers to 20

Write the number

after 13

after 19

after 17

before 17

before 11

before 20

Counting to 20

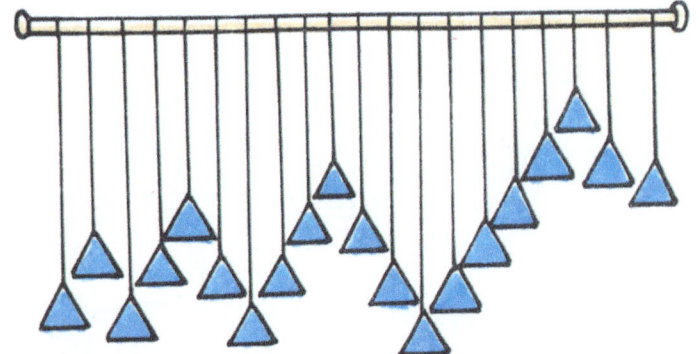

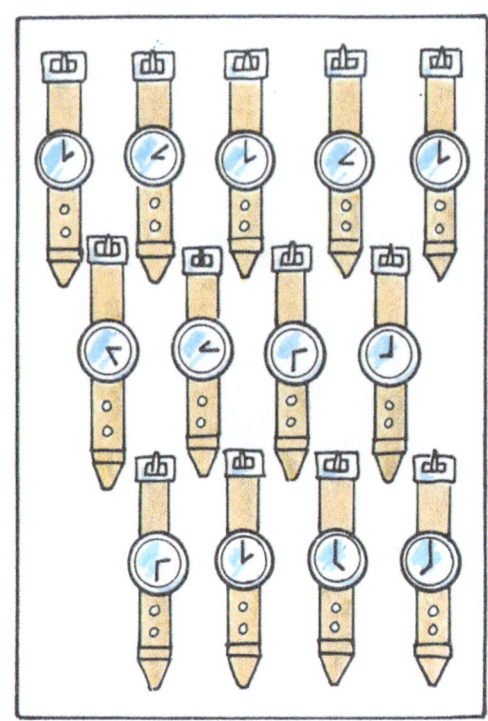

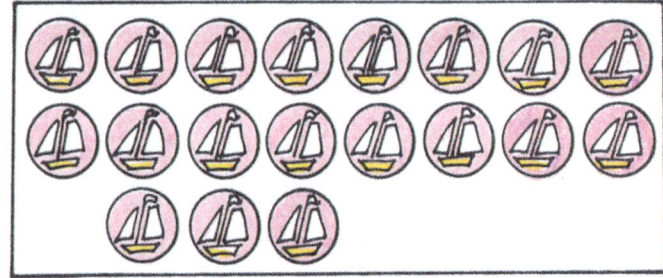

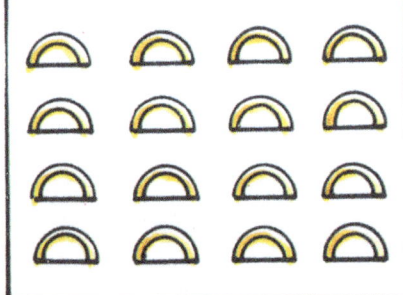
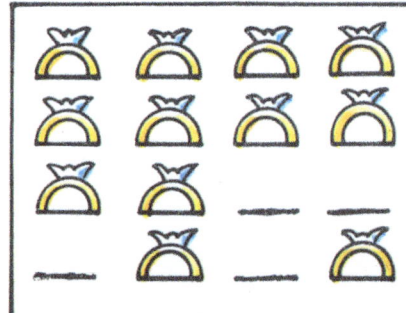

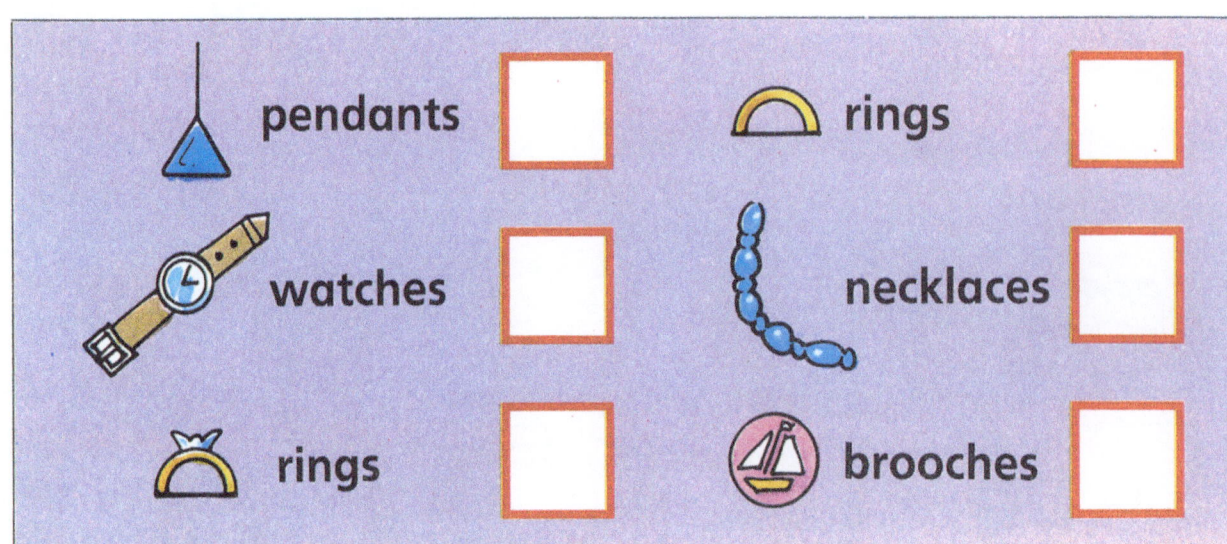

Counting to 20

Jewellery shop

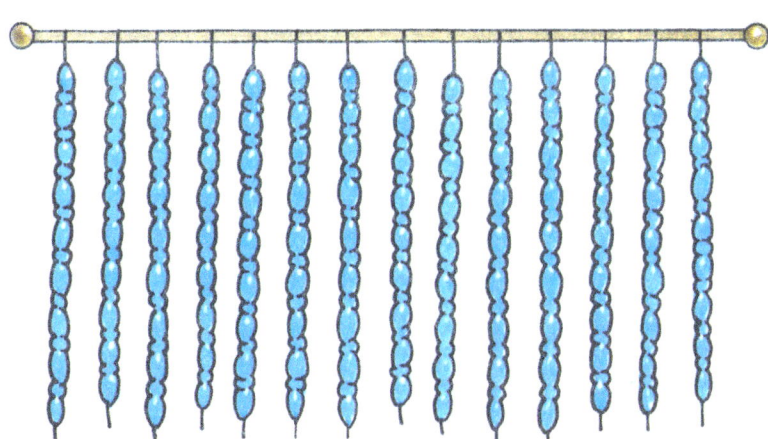
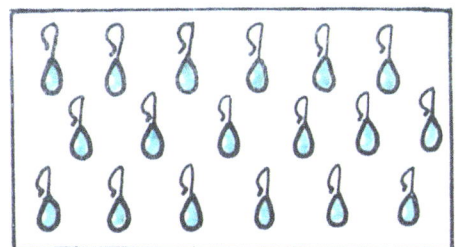

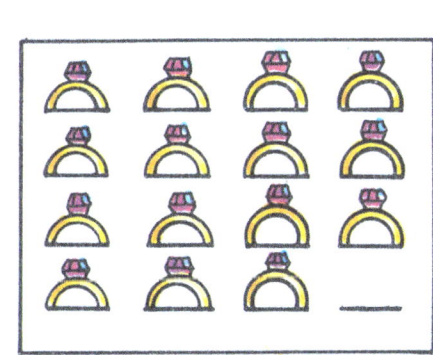
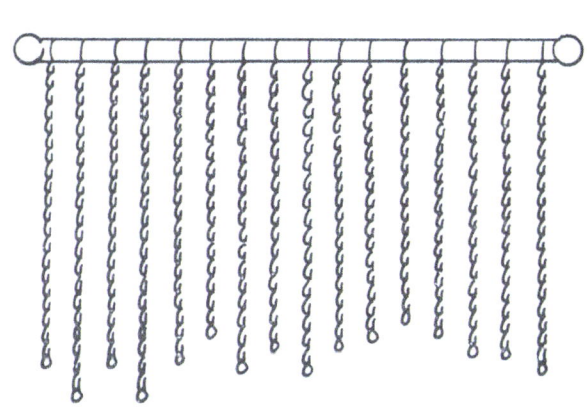

Number names to 20

Write the numbers.

Colour twenty red, twelve blue, thirteen yellow and

Use a calculator to show these numbers.
Write the numbers.

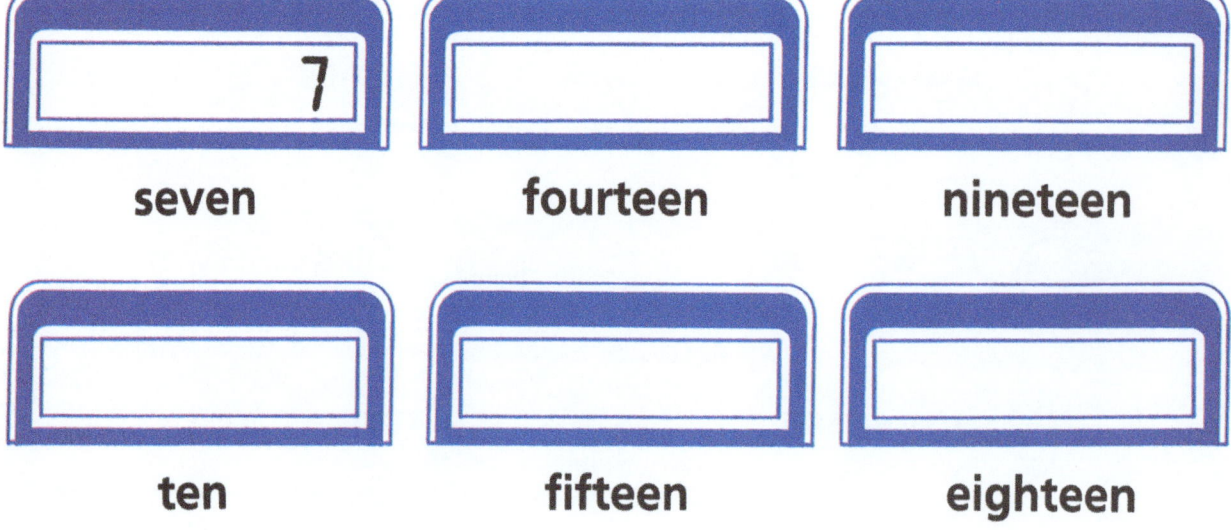

seven   fourteen   nineteen

ten   fifteen   eighteen

names

Number names to 20

sixteen   seventeen   eighteen   nineteen   twenty

seventeen green.

Match

nine
eleven
fourteen
sixteen

The sunflower

Use cubes.

Count out 13.
Put 10 on the  .
13 = 10 and 3

Count out 19.
Put 10 on the  .
19 = 10 and ___

Count out 15.
Put 10 on the   .
15 = 10 and ___

Count out 18.
Put 10 on the  .
18 = 10 and ___

Count out 16.
Put 10 on the  .
16 = ___ and ___

Count out 12.
Put 10 on the   .
12 = ___ and ___

The beanstalk

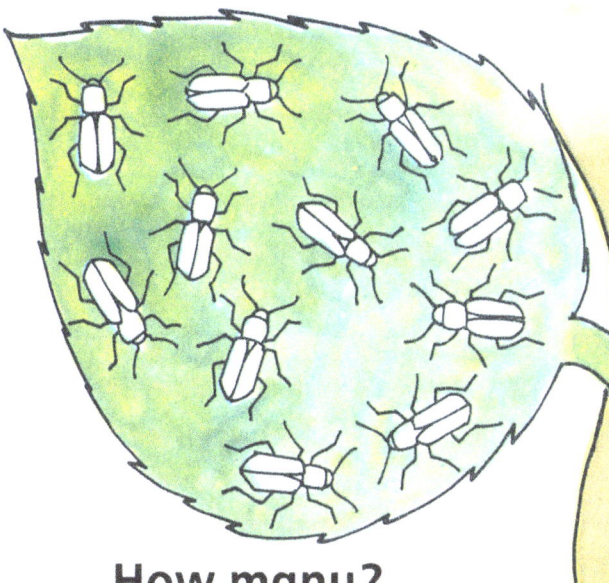

How many? ____
Colour 10 red.

11 = 10 + ____

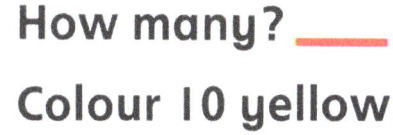

How many? ____
Colour 10 yellow.

14 = 10 + ____

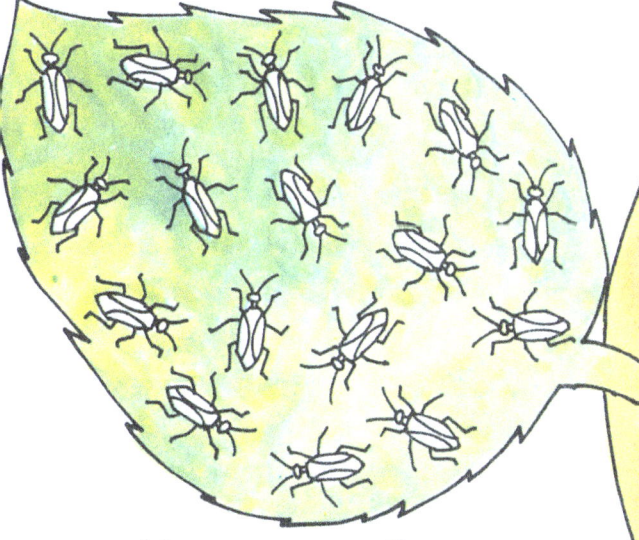

How many? ____
Colour 10 blue.

17 = ____ + ____

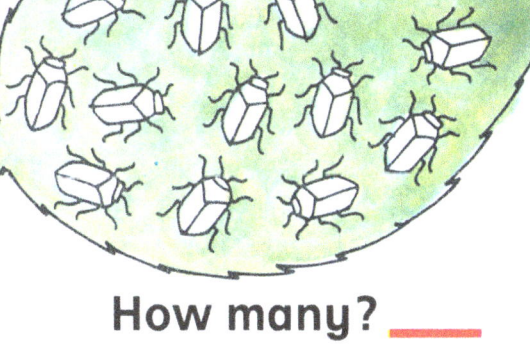

How many? ____
Colour 10 purple.

15 = ____ + ____

19 = ____ + ____
12 = ____ + ____
16 = ____ + ____

The garden centre

   10 + ___

How many altogether?

10 + ___

How many altogether?

10 + ___

How many altogether?

10 + ___

How many altogether?

   10 + ___

How many altogether?

10 + ___

How many altogether?

Loading bricks

Count out 13. Make a ten.

13 = __1__ ten + ____ units

15 = ____ ten + ____ units

18 = ____ ten + ____ units

14 = ____ ten + ____ units

17 = ____ ten + ____ units

19 = ____ ten + ____ units

11 = ____ ten + ____ unit

16 = ____ ten + ____ units

12 = ____ ten + ____ units

20 = ____ tens + ____ units

More bricks

tens

Put out 1 ten and 5 units.
How many cubes altogether? ☐

1 ten + 5 units = ☐

1 ten + 2 units = ☐

1 ten + 7 units = ☐

1 ten + 4 units = ☐

1 ten + 1 unit = ☐

1 ten + 6 units = ☐

2 tens + 0 units = ☐

units

Cranes

Colour the boxes to match the cranes.

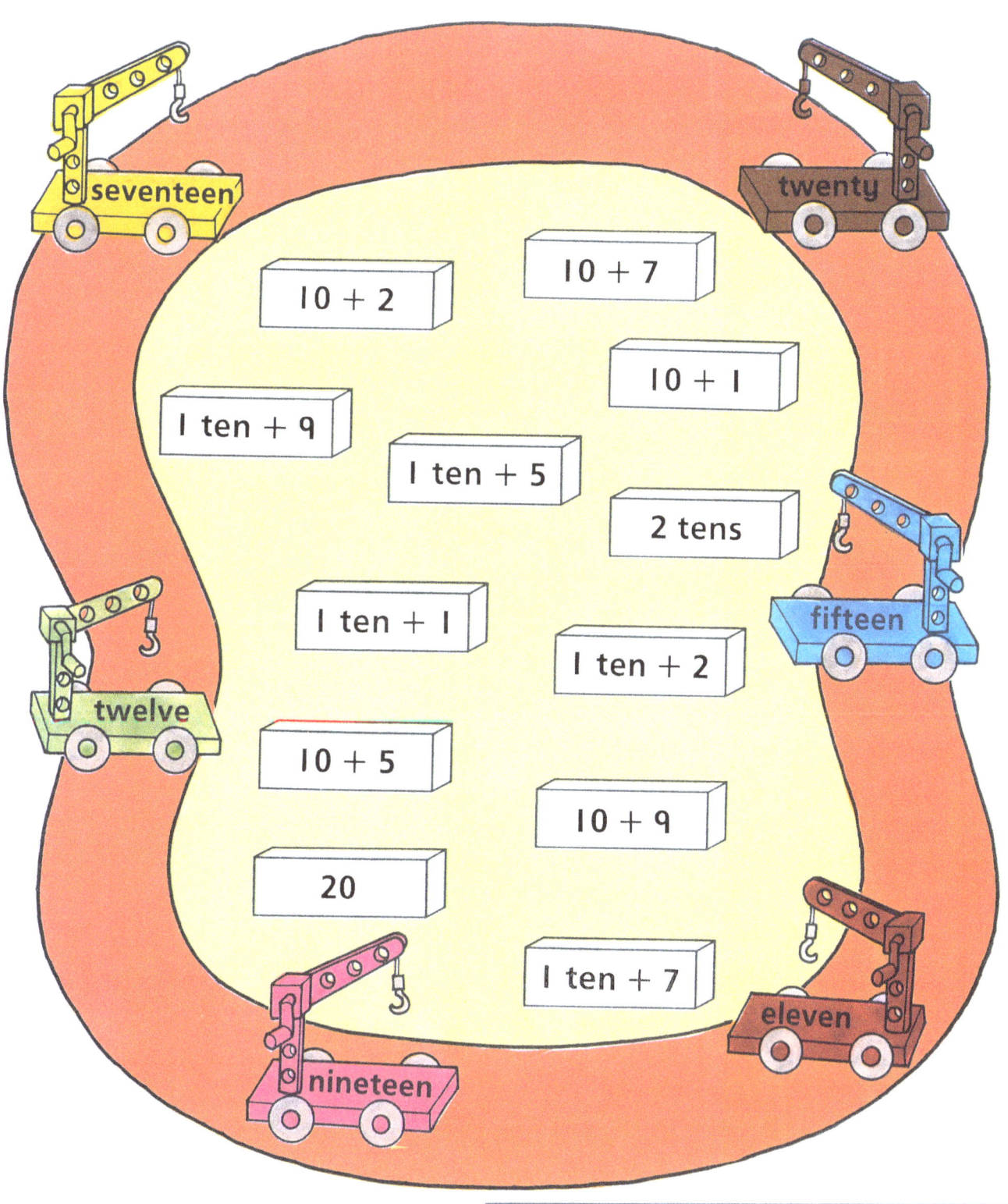

Bunny hops

Start at 4.   Count on 3.   4 + 3 = ☐

Start at 8.   Count on 3.   8 + 3 = ☐

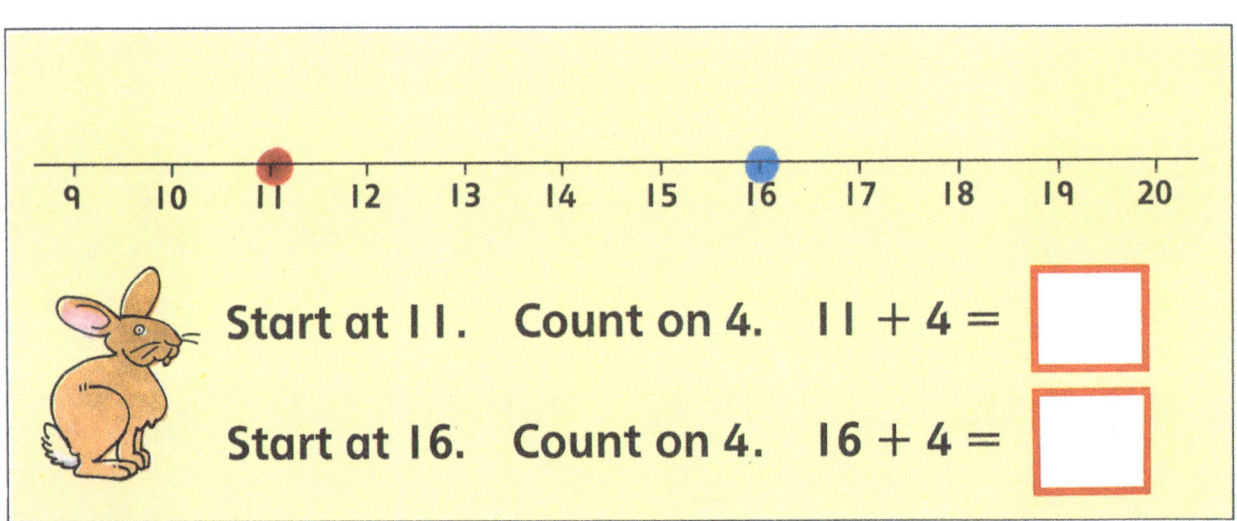

Start at 11.   Count on 4.   11 + 4 = ☐

Start at 16.   Count on 4.   16 + 4 = ☐

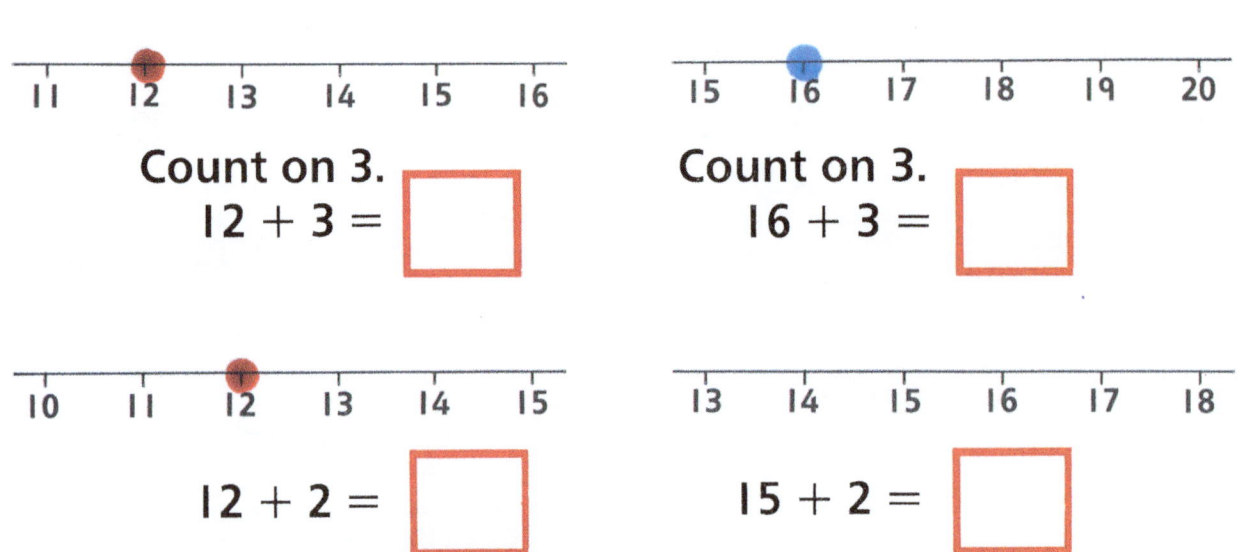

Count on 3.
12 + 3 = ☐

Count on 3.
16 + 3 = ☐

12 + 2 = ☐

15 + 2 = ☐

Party food

Complementary addition

20

Put more cherries on the cake.

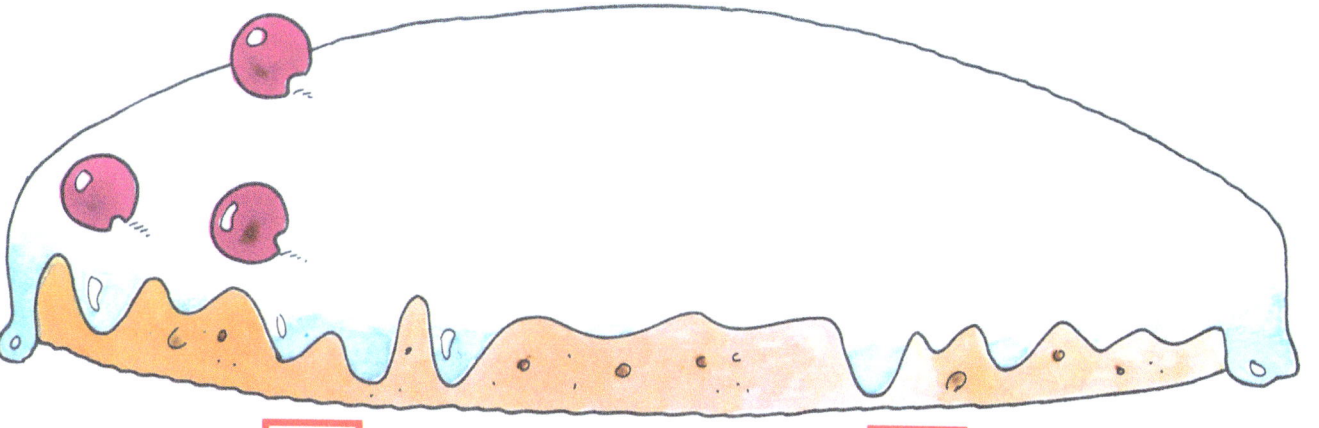

3 + ☐ = 5   3 + ☐ = 4

3 + ☐ = 6   3 + ☐ = 7

3 + ☐ = 9   3 + ☐ = 8

Draw more cakes.   Draw more cakes.

2 + ☐ = 5   5 + ☐ = 8

Draw more apples.   Draw more apples.

 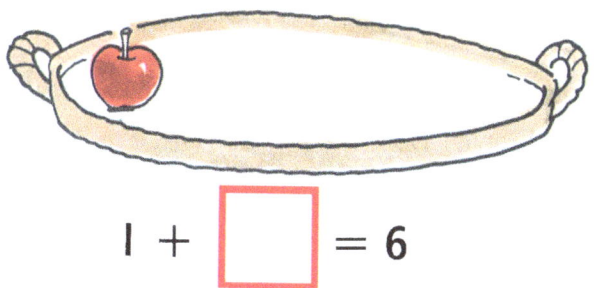

4 + ☐ = 7   1 + ☐ = 6

Complementary addition

Boats

6 + ☐ = 10
4 + ☐ = 10
7 + ☐ = 10
3 + ☐ = 10
9 + ☐ = 10
1 + ☐ = 10
8 + ☐ = 10
2 + ☐ = 10
5 + ☐ = 10

6 + ☐ = 7
5 + ☐ = 9
4 + ☐ = 6

Difference in price

Vegetables

The difference in price is ☐ p.   6 − 4 =

You may use  coins.

    Difference in price ☐ p   8 − 2 =

    Difference in price ☐ p   9 − 6 =

    Difference in price ☐ p

   Difference in price ☐ p

   Difference in price ☐ p

Plants

☐ plants

☐ plants

The difference between 9 and 6 is ___ .   9 − 6 = ☐

☐ trees

☐ trees

The difference between 4 and 8 is ___ .   8 − 4 = ☐

☐ leaves   ☐ leaves

The difference between 7 and 5 is ___ .

7 − 5 = ☐

The difference between 6 and 3 is ___ .

6 − 3 = ☐

The difference between 2 and 9 is ___ .

9 − 2 = ☐

Money to 9p

2

Match the coins.

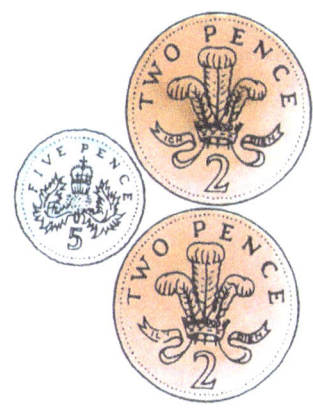

Problem solving

Colour **3** coins to buy a TOFFS.

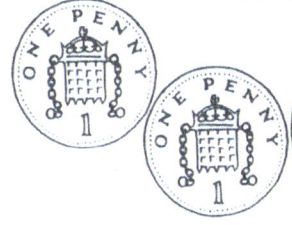

Ten pence

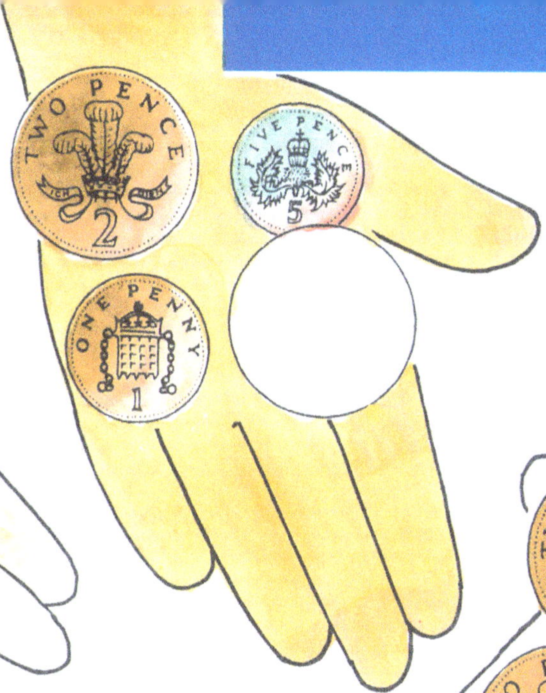

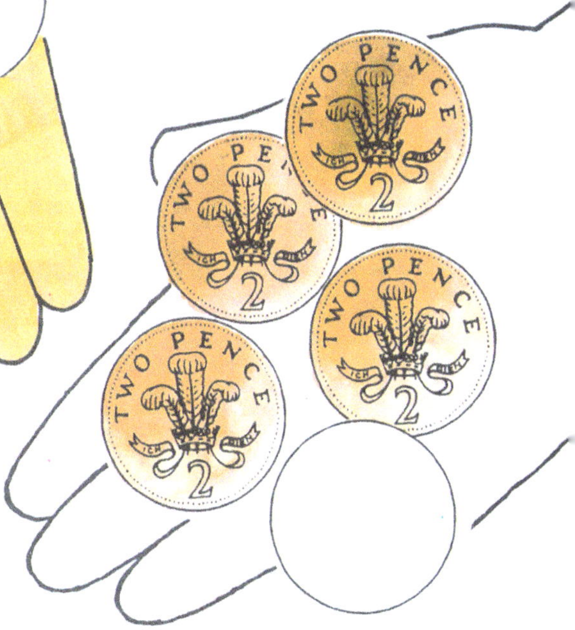

Put out coins. Make each set worth 10p.

Problem solving

Colour coins to make 10p.

Problem solving

Buying things

Tom spends 10p altogether.
Write the price of the boat.

3p   2p

Lili spends 10p.
She buys two things.
Colour their labels.

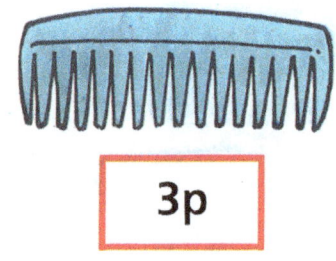

3p

6p

4p

8p

7p

Buying stickers

Use coins. Put out the change.

Change from 5p

Change from 5p

Change from 10p

Change from 10p

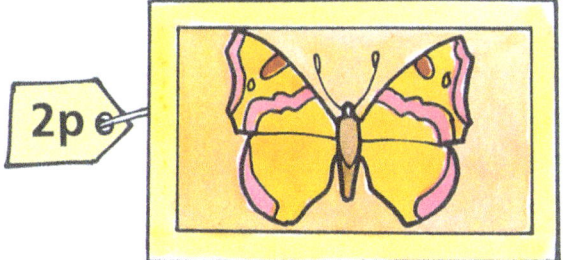

Change from 10p

Counting to 20

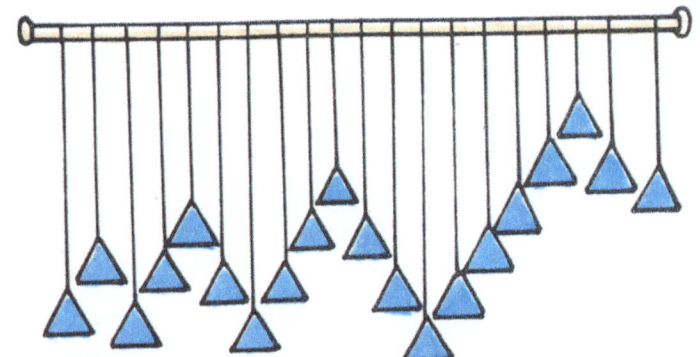
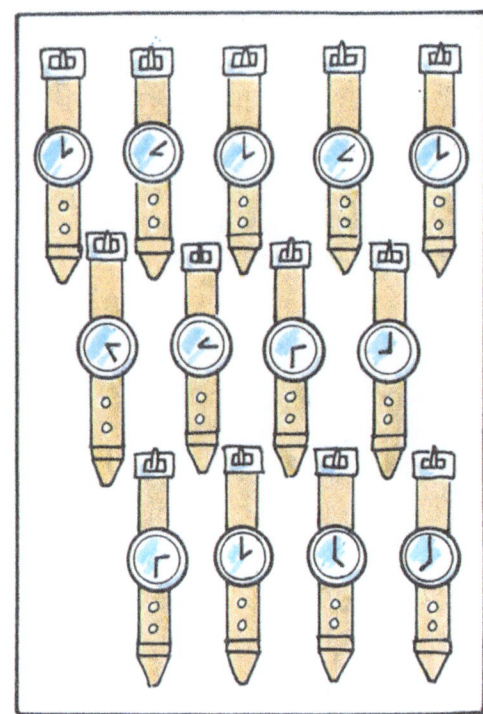

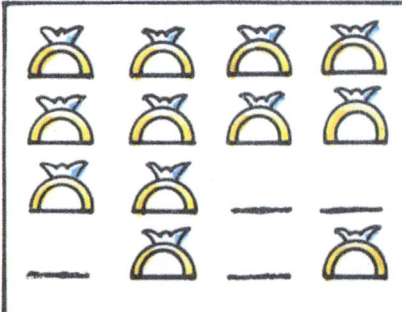

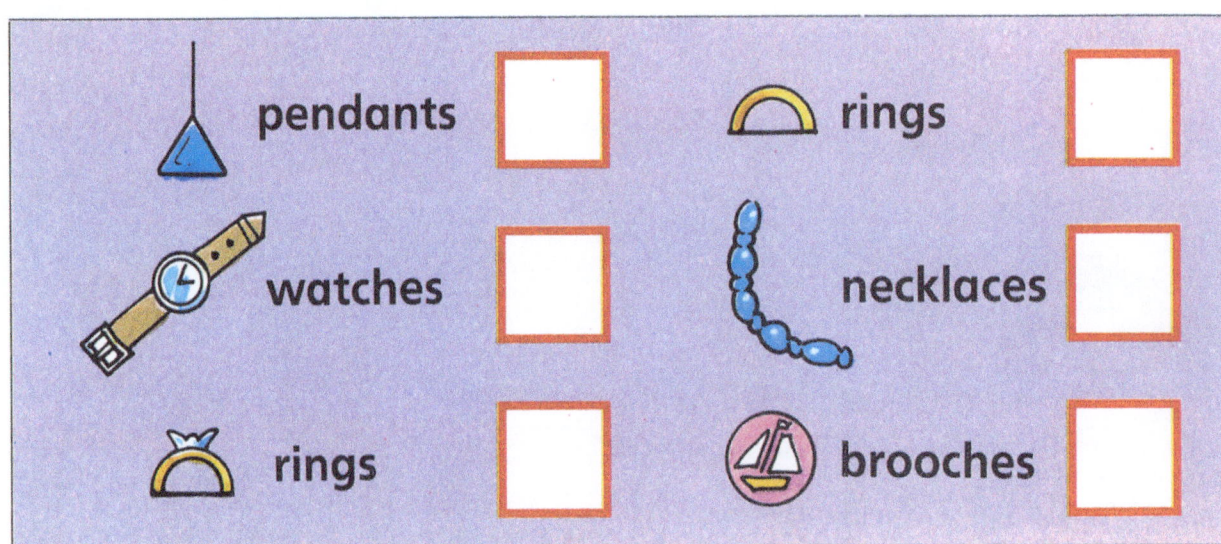

Counting to 20

10

Jewellery shop

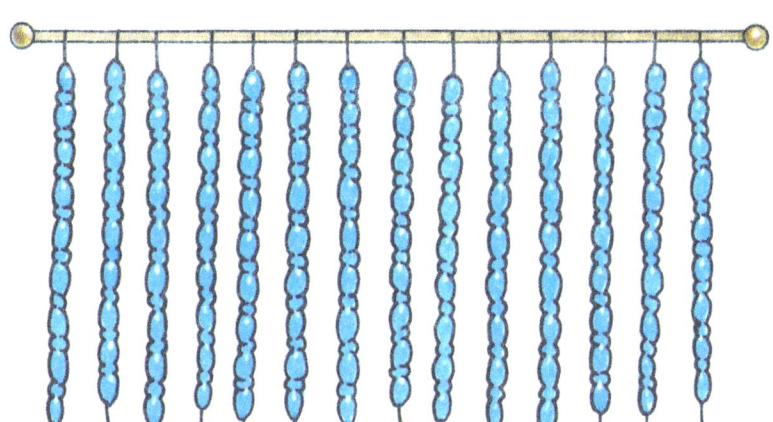
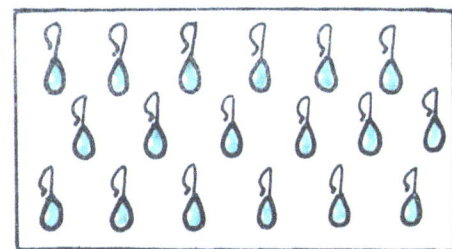

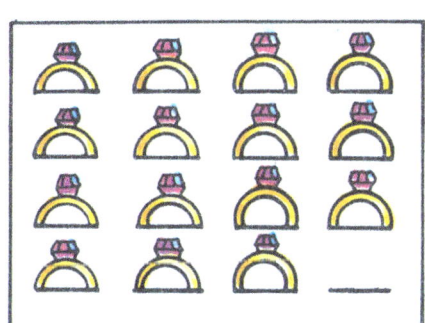
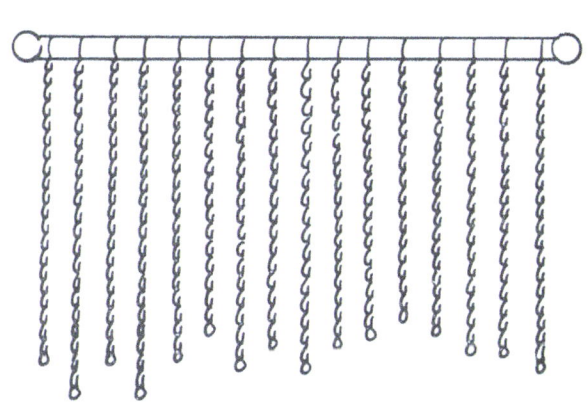
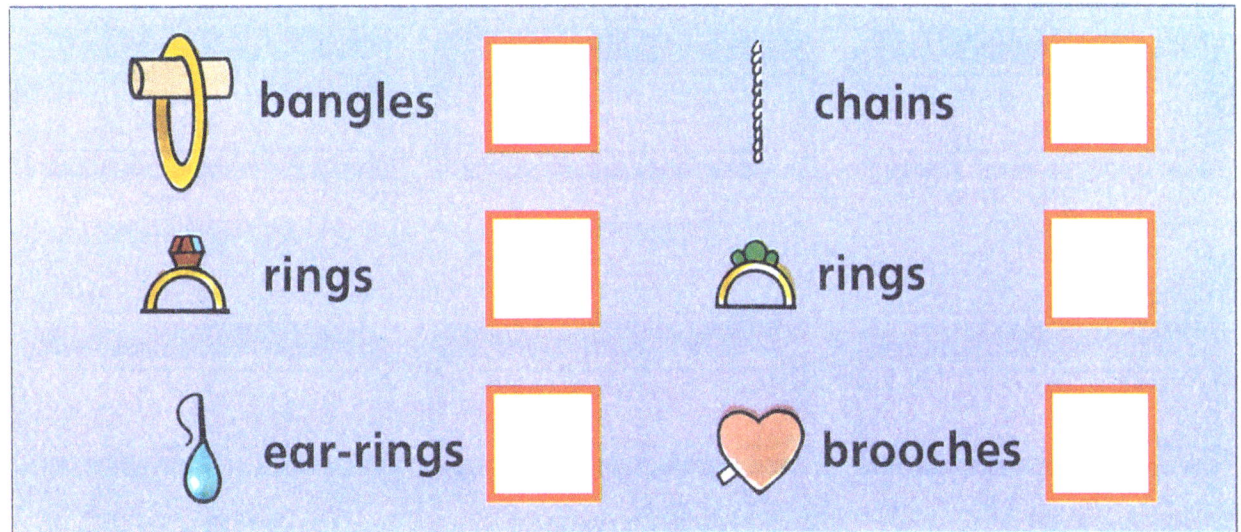

bangles	☐	chains	☐
rings	☐	rings	☐
ear-rings	☐	brooches	☐

Number names to 20

Write the numbers.

Colour twenty red, twelve blue, thirteen yellow and

Use a calculator to show these numbers.
Write the numbers.

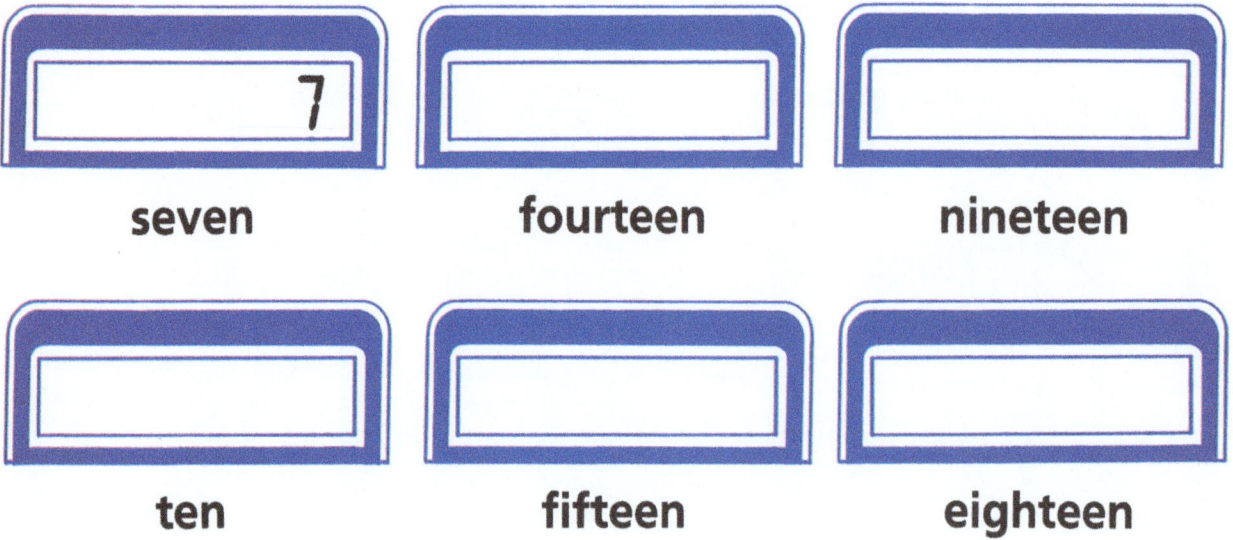

seven   fourteen   nineteen

ten   fifteen   eighteen

Number names to 20

12

sixteen   seventeen   eighteen   nineteen   twenty

seventeen green.

Match

nine
eleven
fourteen
sixteen

The sunflower

Use cubes.

Count out 13.
Put 10 on the  .
13 = 10 and 3

Count out 19.
Put 10 on the   .
19 = 10 and ___

Count out 15.
Put 10 on the  .
15 = 10 and ___

Count out 18.
Put 10 on the  .
18 = 10 and ___

Count out 16.
Put 10 on the  .
16 = ___ and ___

Count out 12.
Put 10 on the   .
12 = ___ and ___

The beanstalk

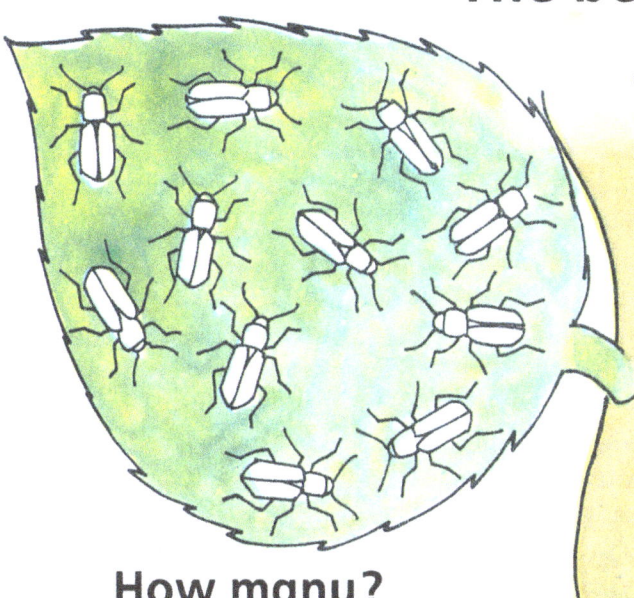

How many? ____
Colour 10 red.

11 = 10 + ____

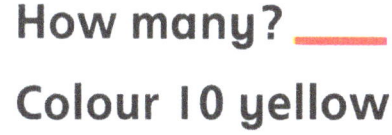

How many? ____
Colour 10 yellow.

14 = 10 + ____

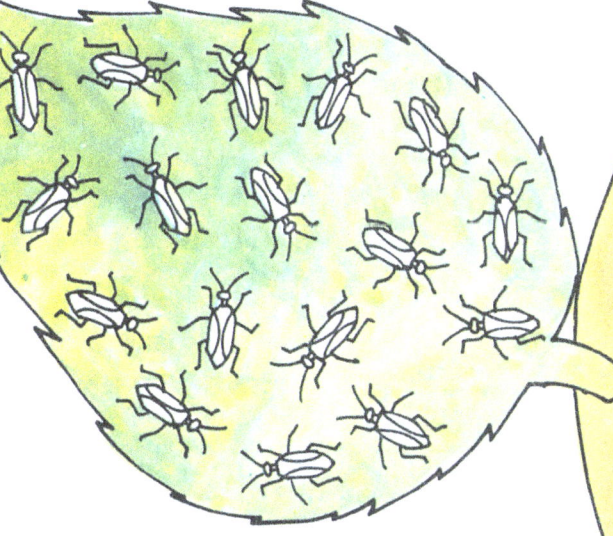

How many? ____
Colour 10 blue.

17 = ____ + ____

How many? ____
Colour 10 purple.

15 = ____ + ____

19 = ____ + ____
12 = ____ + ____
16 = ____ + ____

Towards place value

The garden centre

10 plants

10 + ___

How many altogether? ☐

10 canes

10 + ___

How many altogether? ☐

10 roses

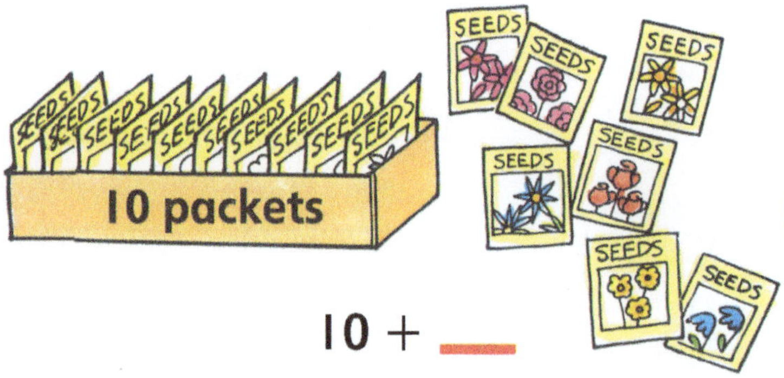

10 + ___

How many altogether? ☐

10 pots

10 + ___

How many altogether? ☐

10 packets

10 + ___

How many altogether? ☐

10 bulbs

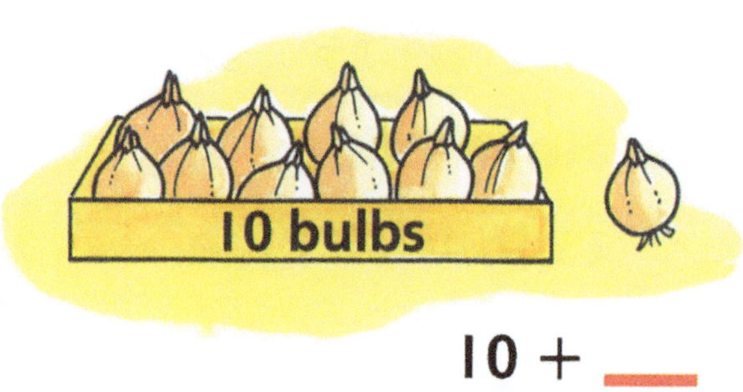

10 + ___

How many altogether? ☐

Loading bricks

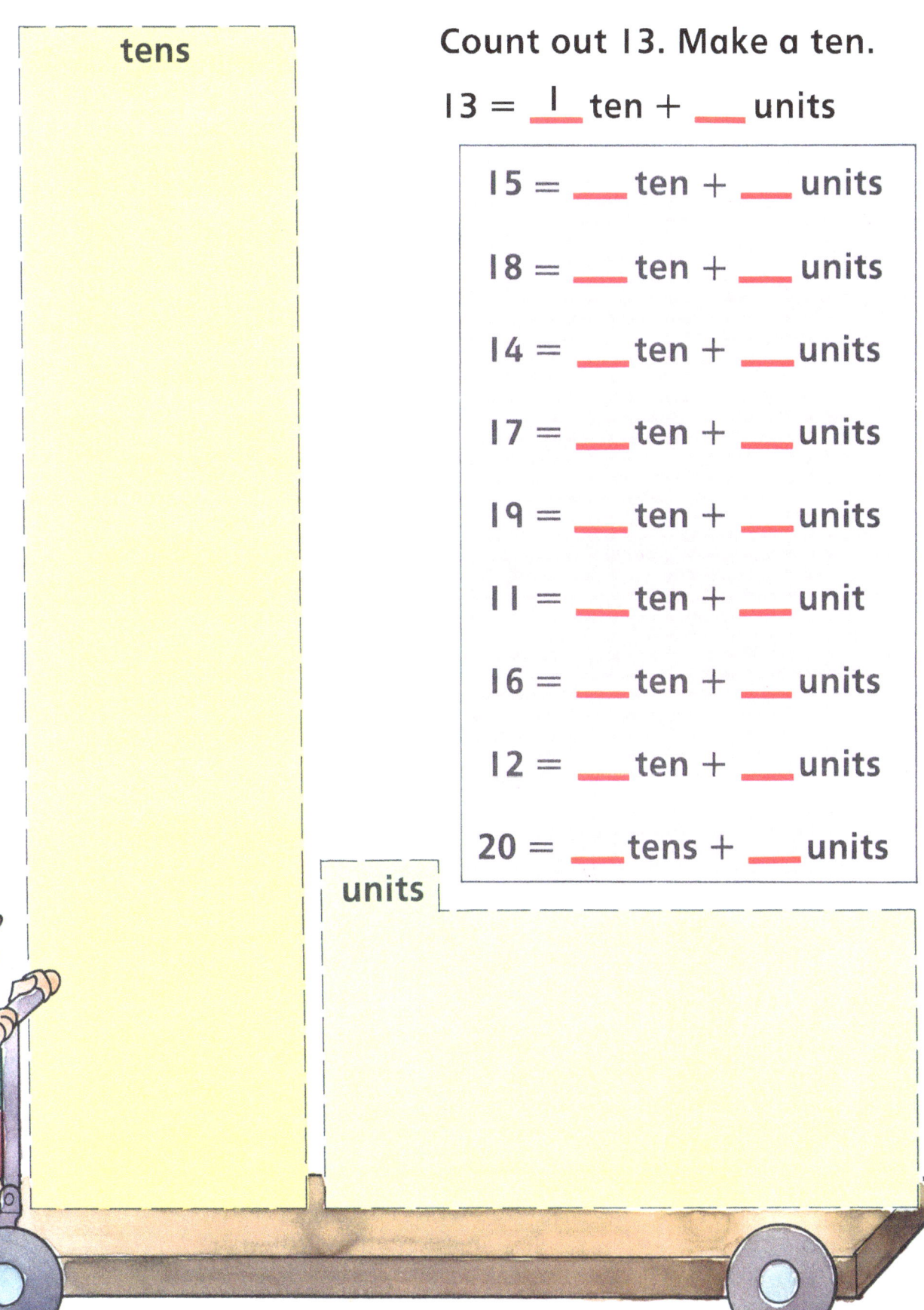

Count out 13. Make a ten.

13 = __1__ ten + ____ units

15 = ____ ten + ____ units

18 = ____ ten + ____ units

14 = ____ ten + ____ units

17 = ____ ten + ____ units

19 = ____ ten + ____ units

11 = ____ ten + ____ unit

16 = ____ ten + ____ units

12 = ____ ten + ____ units

20 = ____ tens + ____ units

Place value to 20

More bricks

Put out 1 ten and 5 units.
How many cubes altogether? ☐

1 ten + 5 units = ☐

1 ten + 2 units = ☐

1 ten + 7 units = ☐

1 ten + 4 units = ☐

1 ten + 1 unit = ☐

1 ten + 6 units = ☐

2 tens + 0 units = ☐

Cranes

Colour the boxes to match the cranes.

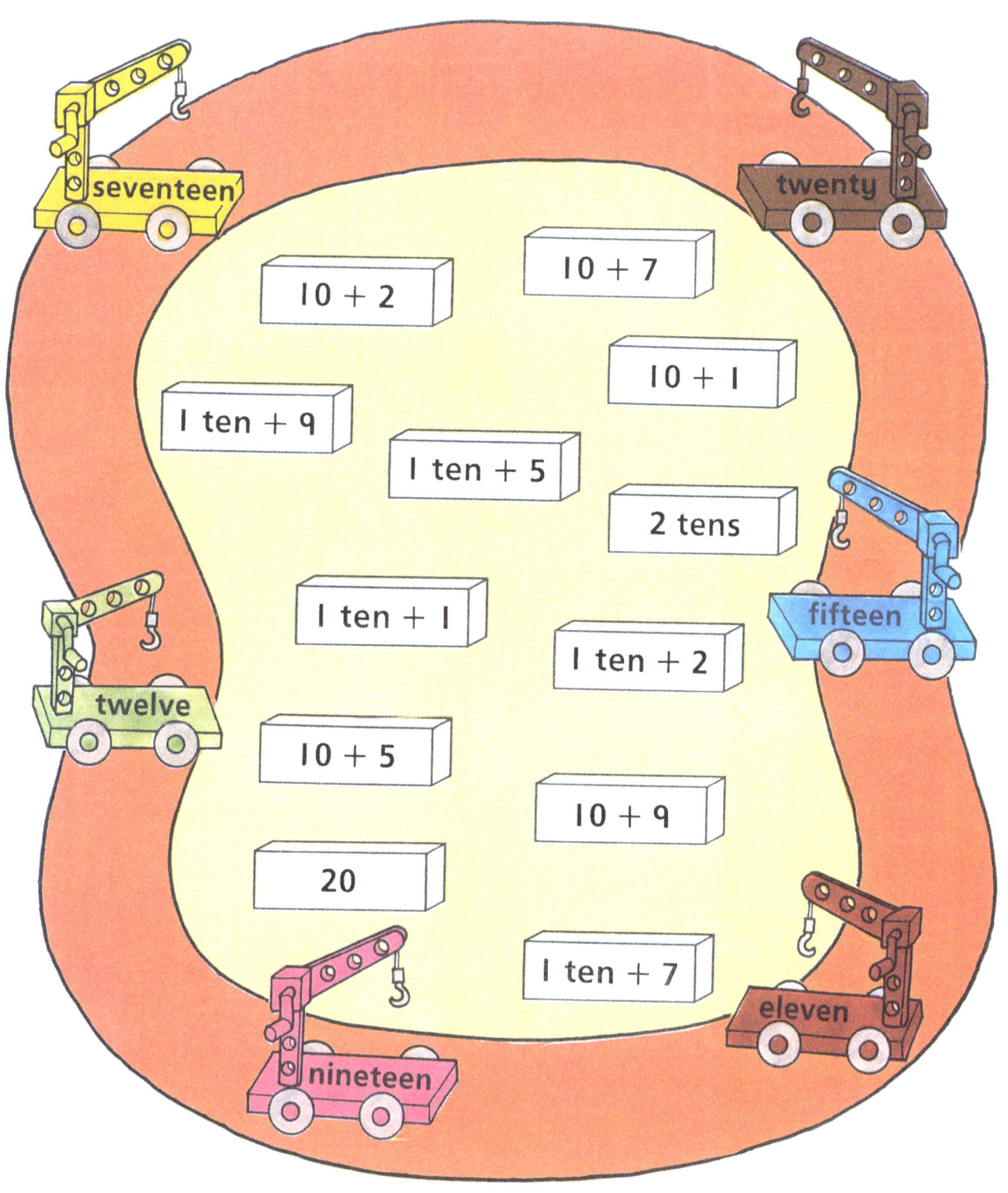

Bunny hops

Start at 4.   Count on 3.   4 + 3 = ☐

Start at 8.   Count on 3.   8 + 3 = ☐

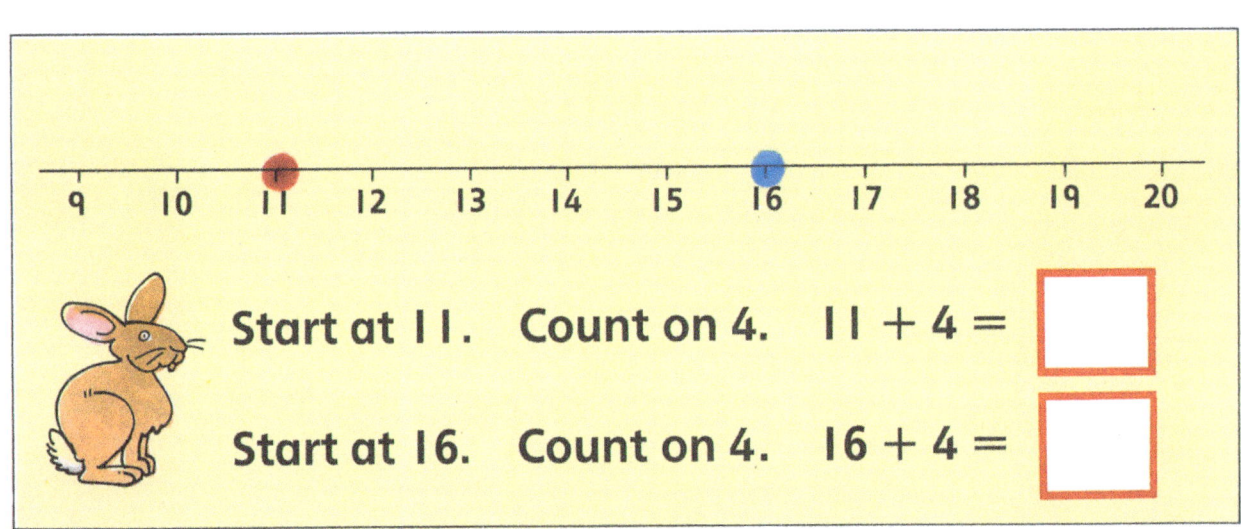

Start at 11.   Count on 4.   11 + 4 = ☐

Start at 16.   Count on 4.   16 + 4 = ☐

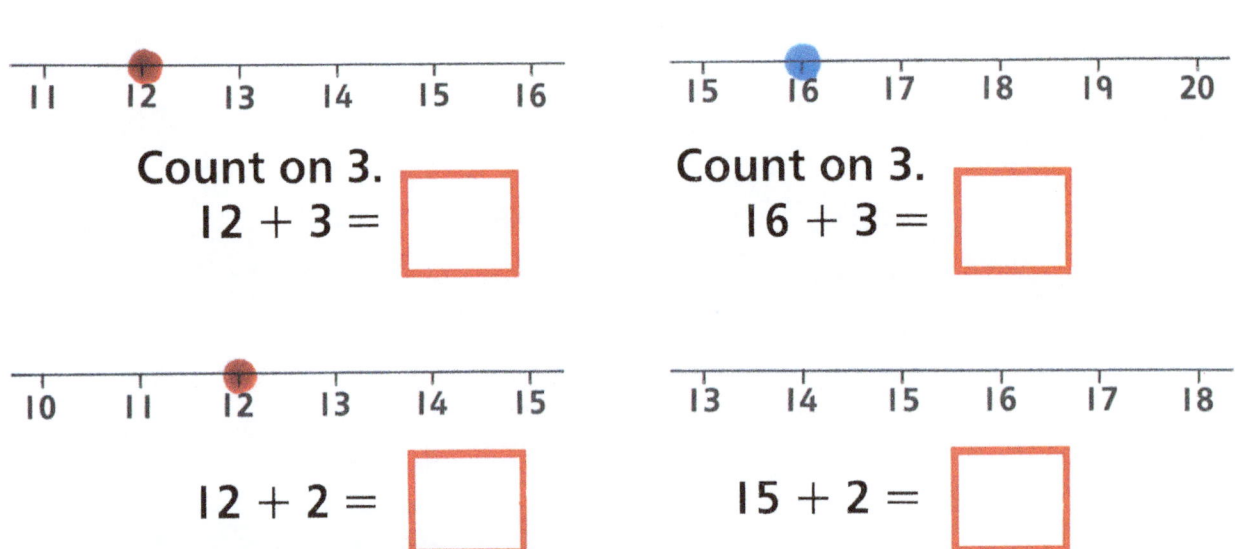

Count on 3.
12 + 3 = ☐

Count on 3.
16 + 3 = ☐

12 + 2 = ☐

15 + 2 = ☐

Complementary addition

Party food

Put more cherries on the cake.

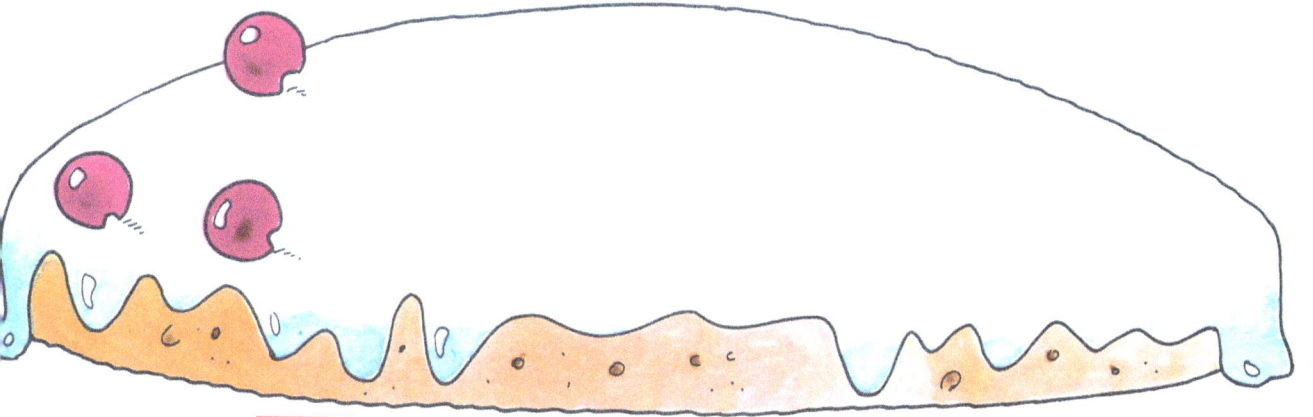

3 + ☐ = 5   3 + ☐ = 4

3 + ☐ = 6   3 + ☐ = 7

3 + ☐ = 9   3 + ☐ = 8

Draw more cakes.   Draw more cakes.

2 + ☐ = 5   5 + ☐ = 8

Draw more apples.   Draw more apples.

   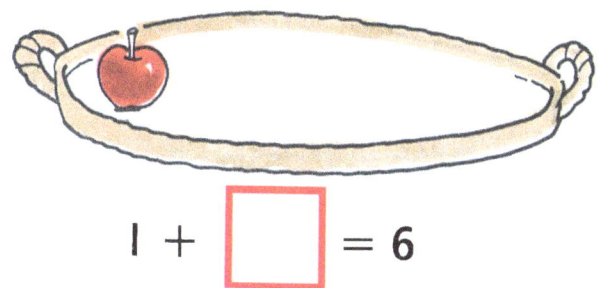

4 + ☐ = 7   1 + ☐ = 6

Boats

Vegetables

Difference in price

The difference in price is ☐ p.   6 – 4 =

You may use 🪙 coins.

 Difference in price ☐ p   8 – 2 =

 Difference in price ☐ p   9 – 6 =

Difference in price ☐ p

Difference in price ☐ p

Difference in price ☐ p

Plants

☐ plants
☐ plants

The difference between 9 and 6 is ___ .   9 − 6 = ☐

☐ trees
☐ trees

The difference between 4 and 8 is ___ .   8 − 4 = ☐

☐ leaves   ☐ leaves

The difference between 7 and 5 is ___ .

7 − 5 = ☐

The difference between 6 and 3 is ___ .

6 − 3 = ☐

The difference between 2 and 9 is ___ .

9 − 2 = ☐

Money to 9p

Match the coins.

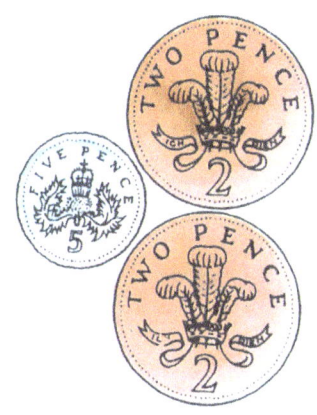

Problem solving

Colour 3 coins to buy a TOFFS.

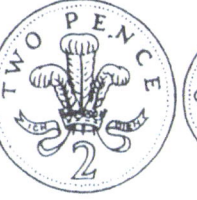

Ten pence

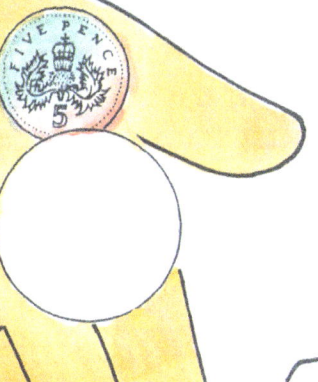

Put out coins.
Make each set worth

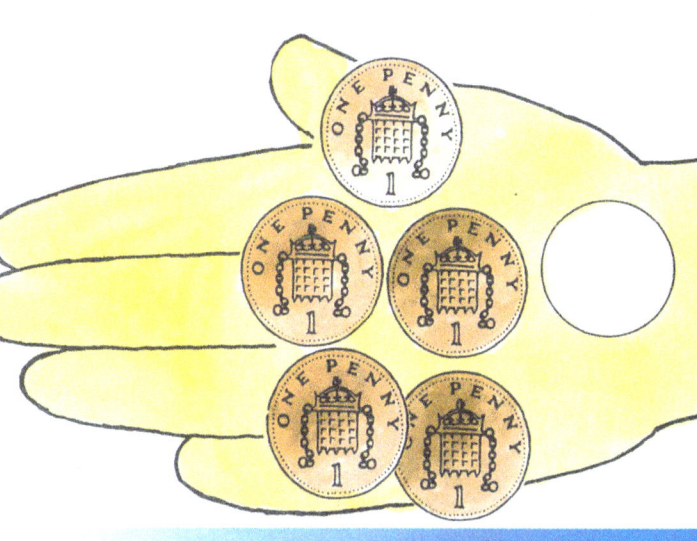

Colour coins to make 10p.

     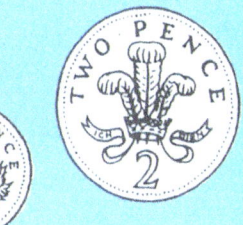

Problem solving

Buying things

Tom spends 10p altogether.
Write the price of the boat.

3p   2p

Lili spends 10p.
She buys two things.
Colour their labels.

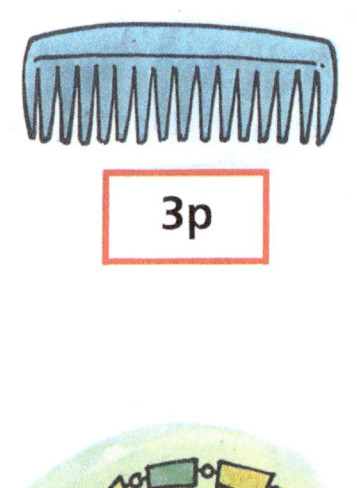

3p

6p

4p

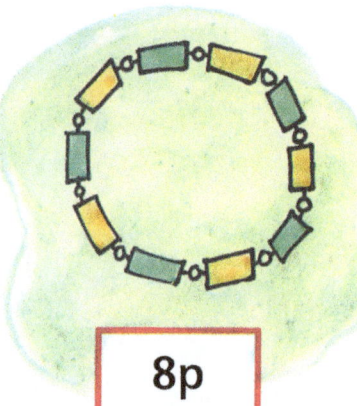

8p

7p

Change from 5p and 10p

Buying stickers

Use coins. Put out the change.

R6

Change from 5p

Change from 5p

Change from 10p

Change from 10p

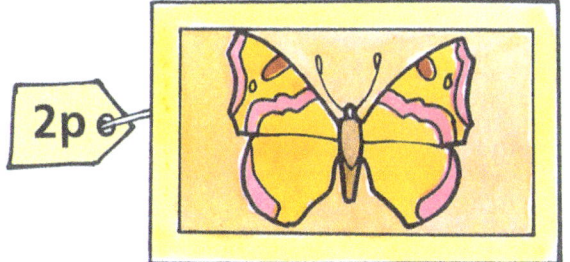

Change from 10p

R7,8

Counting to 20

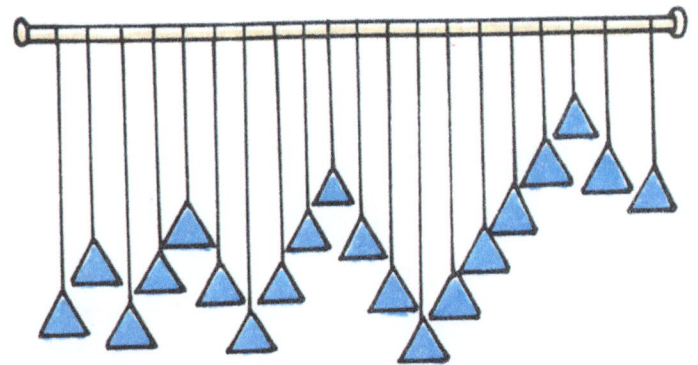

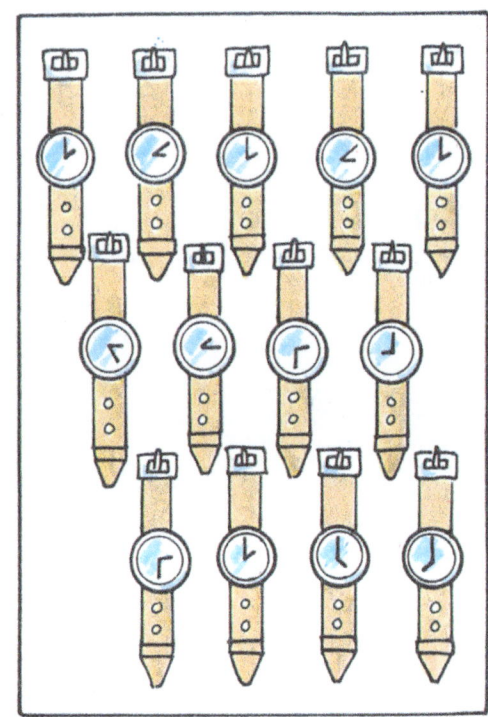

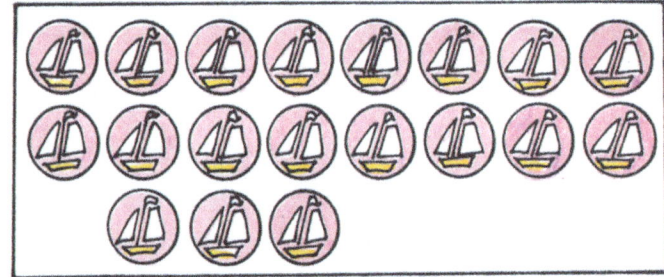

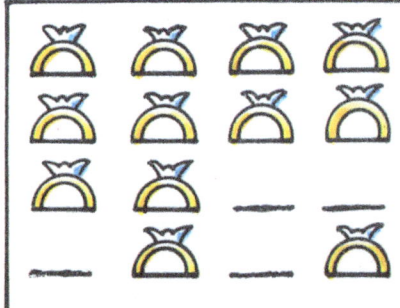

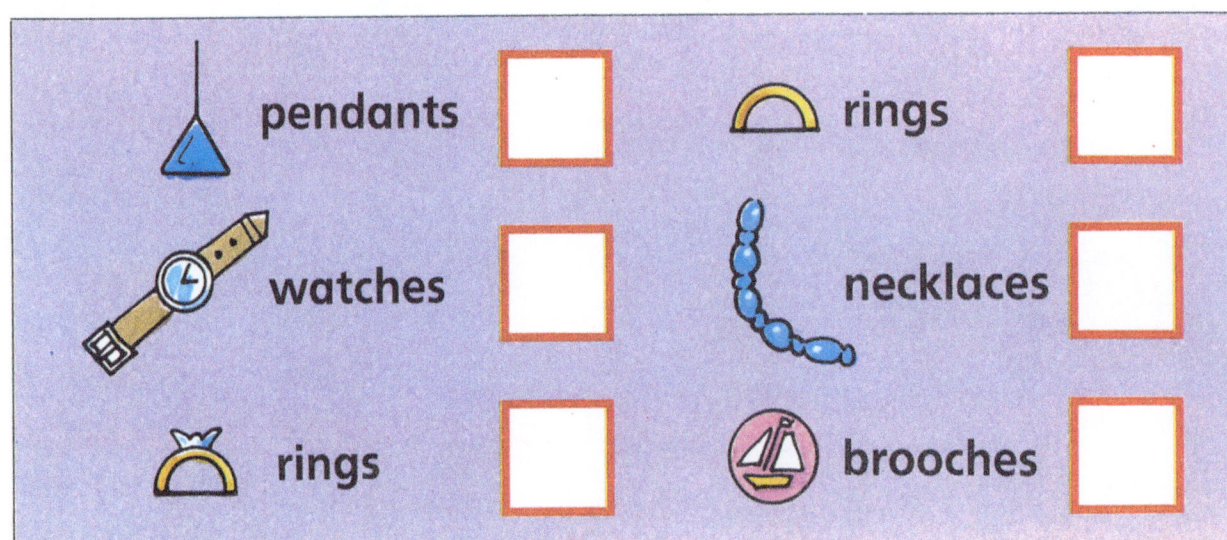

pendants ☐   rings ☐

watches ☐   necklaces ☐

rings ☐   brooches ☐

Jewellery shop

Counting to 20

10

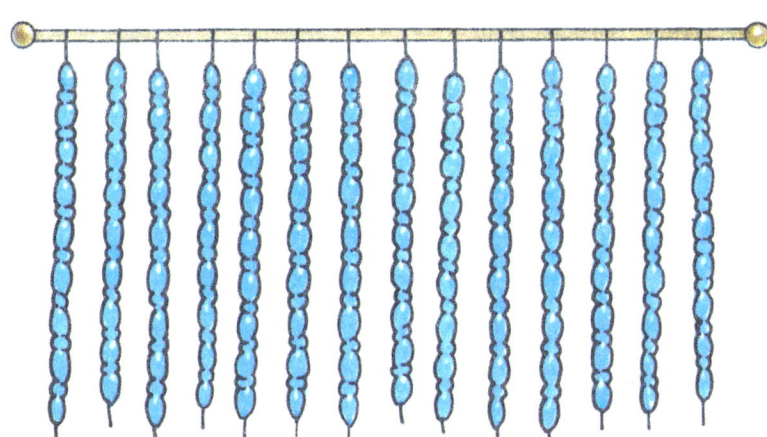
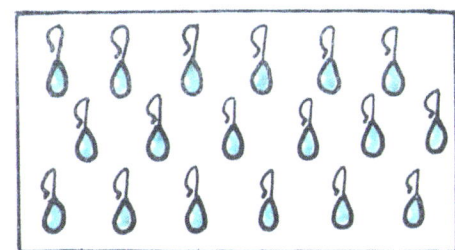
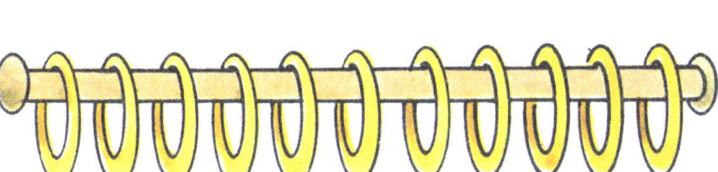

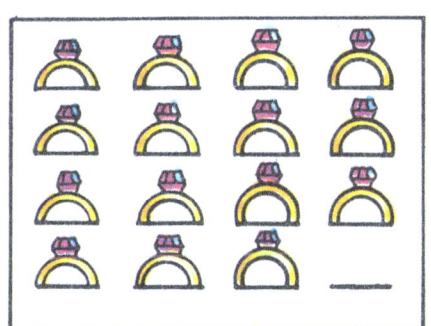
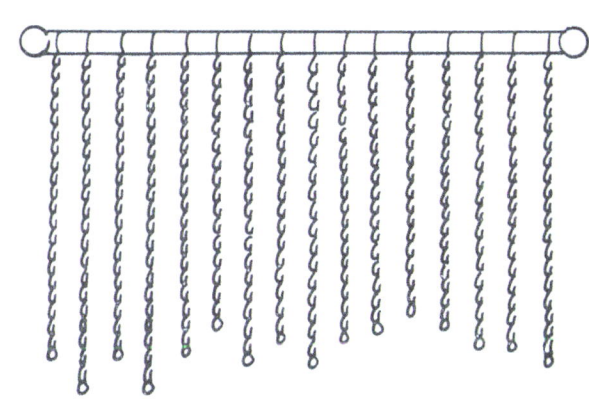
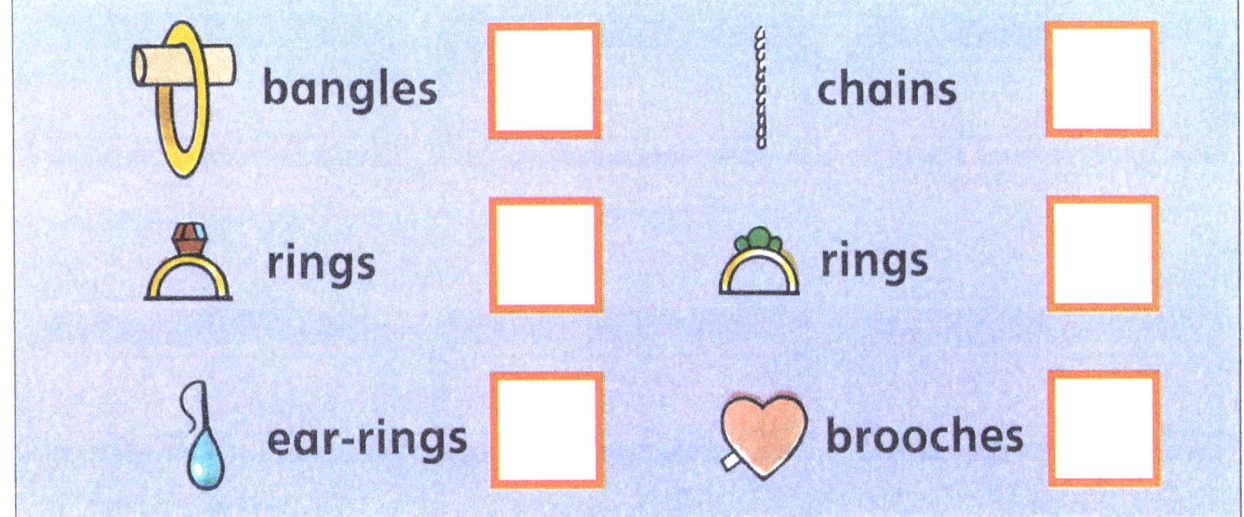

bangles ☐   chains ☐

rings ☐   rings ☐

ear-rings ☐   brooches ☐

Write the numbers.

Colour twenty red, twelve blue, thirteen yellow and

**Use a calculator to show these numbers.
Write the numbers.**

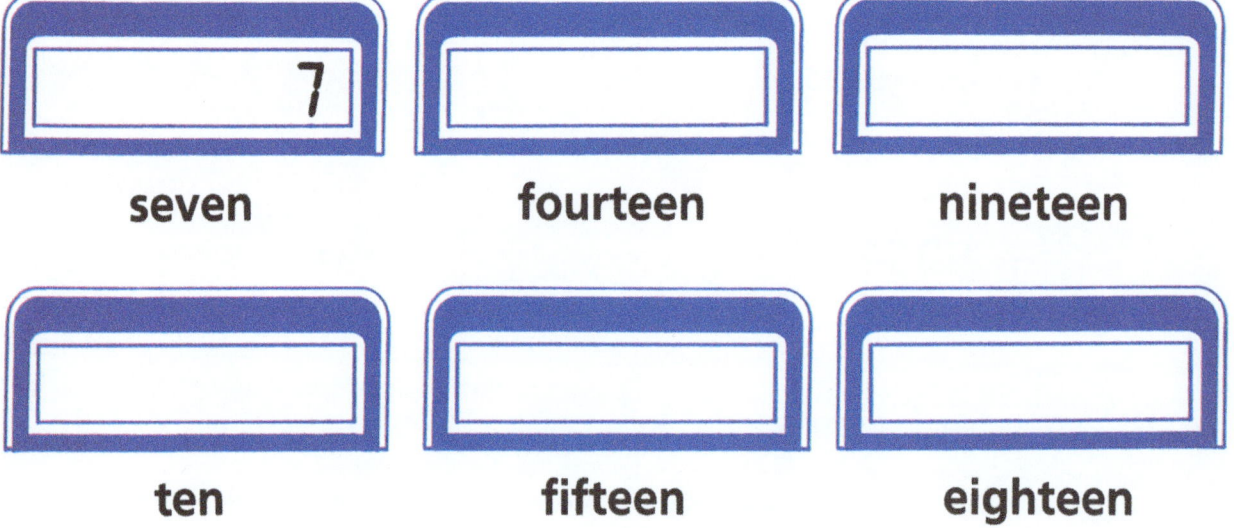

seven   fourteen   nineteen

ten   fifteen   eighteen

Number names to 20

12

sixteen seventeen eighteen nineteen twenty

seventeen green.

Match

nine
eleven
fourteen
sixteen

The sunflower

Use cubes.

Count out 13.
Put 10 on the  .
13 = 10 and 3

Count out 19.
Put 10 on the  .
19 = 10 and ___

Count out 15.
Put 10 on the  .
15 = 10 and ___

Count out 18.
Put 10 on the  .
18 = 10 and ___

Count out 16.
Put 10 on the   .
16 = ___ and ___

Count out 12.
Put 10 on the   .
12 = ___ and ___

The beanstalk

Towards place value

14

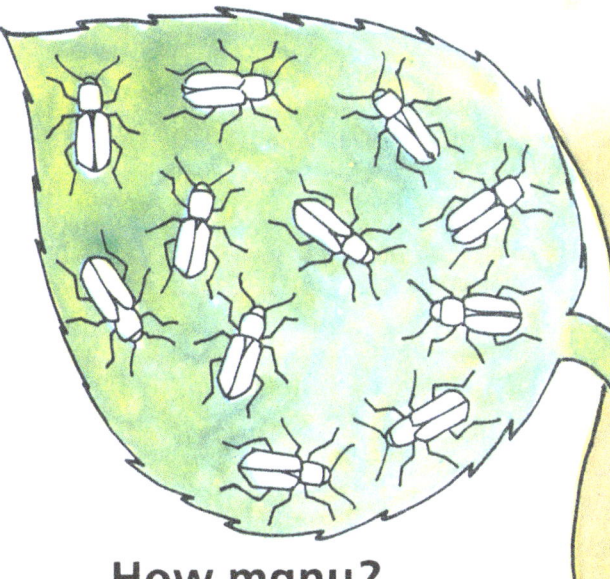

How many? ___
Colour 10 red.

11 = 10 + ___

How many? ___
Colour 10 yellow.

14 = 10 + ___

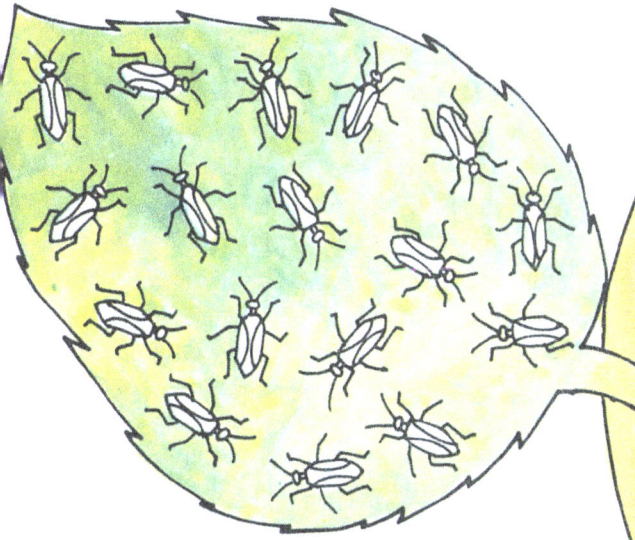

How many? ___
Colour 10 blue.

17 = ___ + ___

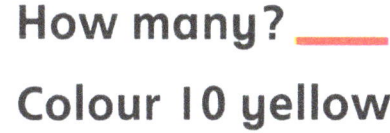

How many? ___
Colour 10 purple.

15 = ___ + ___

19 = ___ + ___
12 = ___ + ___
16 = ___ + ___

The garden centre

10 + ___

How many altogether? ☐

10 + ___

How many altogether? ☐

10 + ___

How many altogether? ☐

10 + ___

How many altogether? ☐

10 + ___

How many altogether? ☐

10 + ___

How many altogether? ☐

Loading bricks

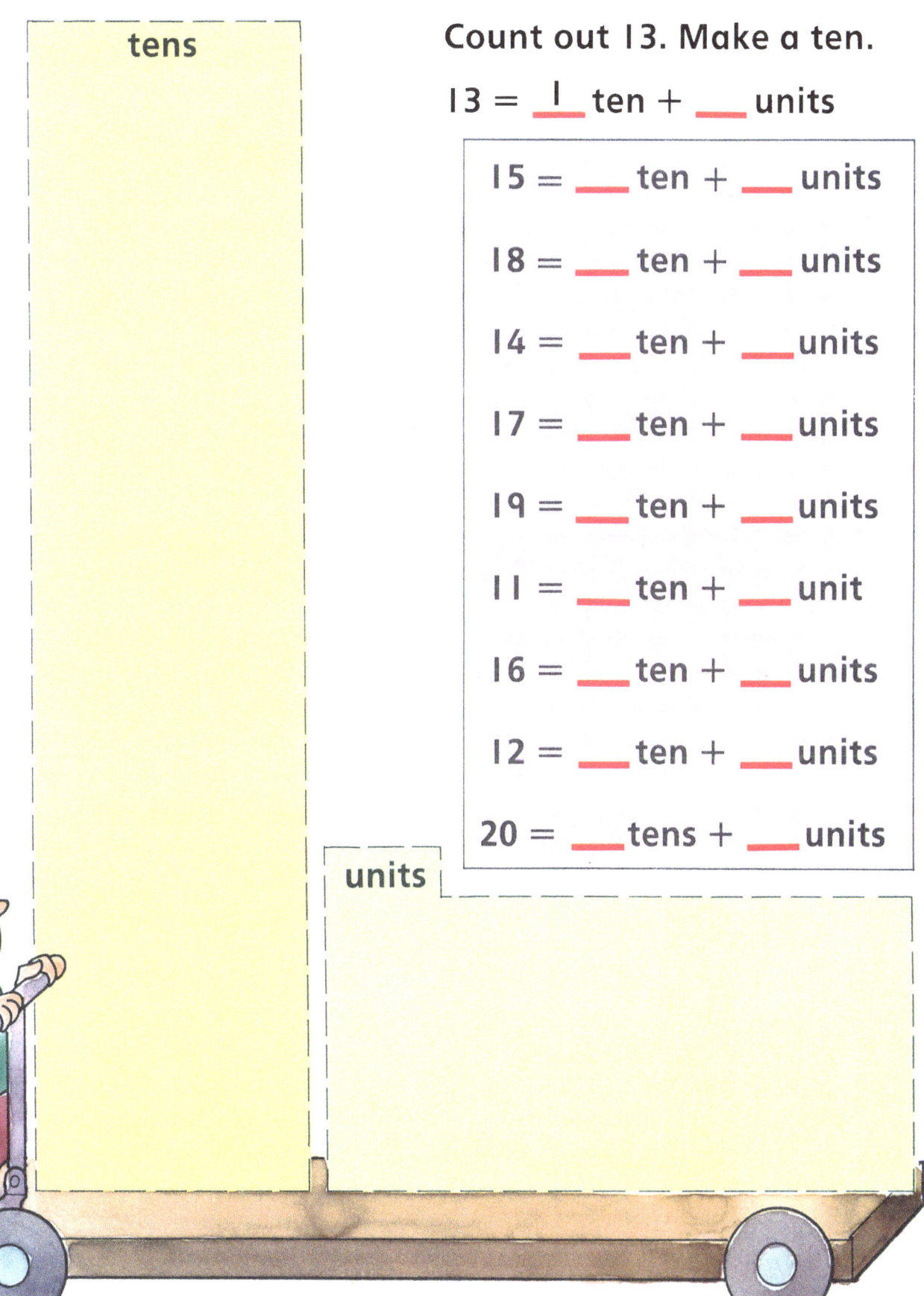

Count out 13. Make a ten.

13 = __1__ ten + ____ units

15 = ____ ten + ____ units

18 = ____ ten + ____ units

14 = ____ ten + ____ units

17 = ____ ten + ____ units

19 = ____ ten + ____ units

11 = ____ ten + ____ unit

16 = ____ ten + ____ units

12 = ____ ten + ____ units

20 = ____ tens + ____ units

More bricks

Place value to 20

tens

units

Put out 1 ten and 5 units.
How many cubes altogether? ☐

1 ten + 5 units = ☐

1 ten + 2 units = ☐

1 ten + 7 units = ☐

1 ten + 4 units = ☐

1 ten + 1 unit = ☐

1 ten + 6 units = ☐

2 tens + 0 units = ☐

Cranes

Colour the boxes to match the cranes.

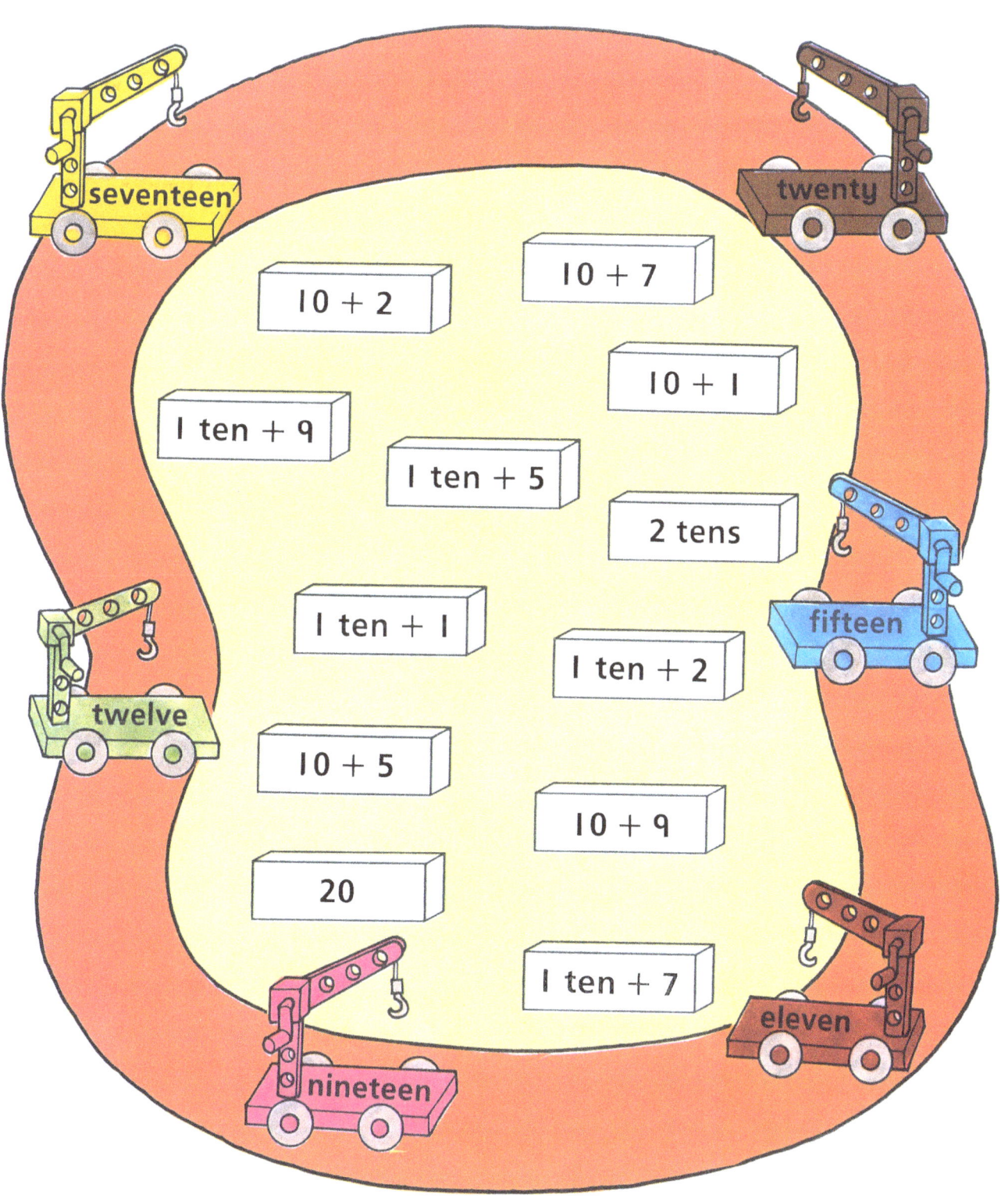

Bunny hops

Start at 4.   Count on 3.   4 + 3 = ☐

Start at 8.   Count on 3.   8 + 3 = ☐

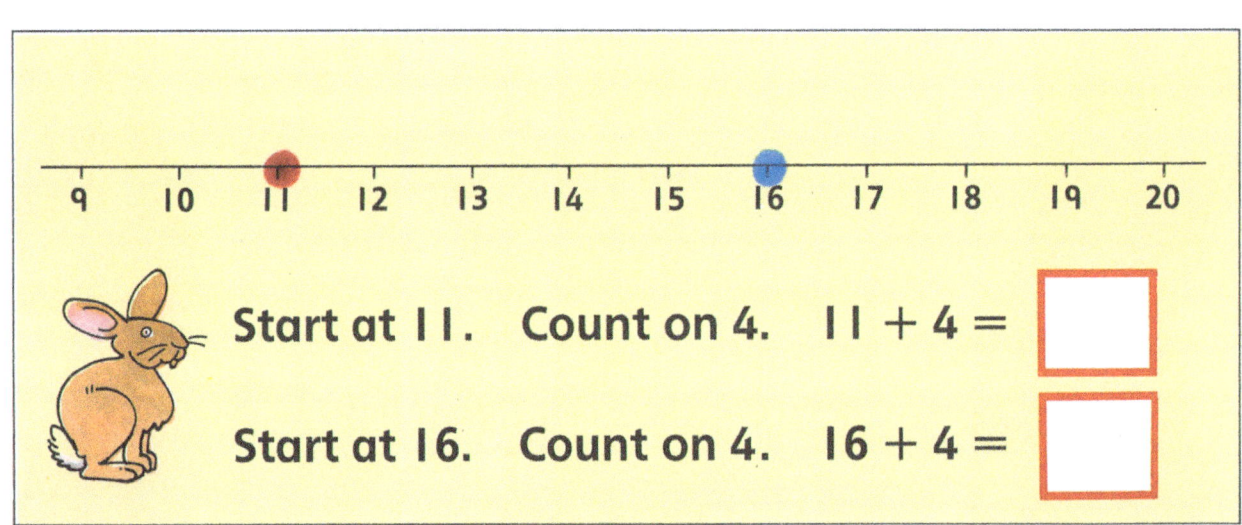

Start at 11.   Count on 4.   11 + 4 = ☐

Start at 16.   Count on 4.   16 + 4 = ☐

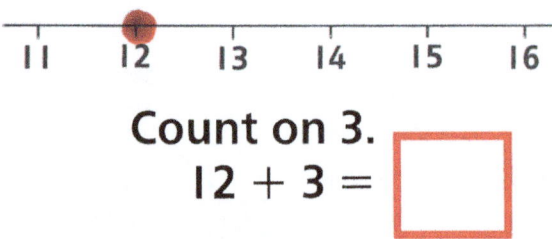 

Count on 3.   12 + 3 = ☐

Count on 3.   16 + 3 = ☐

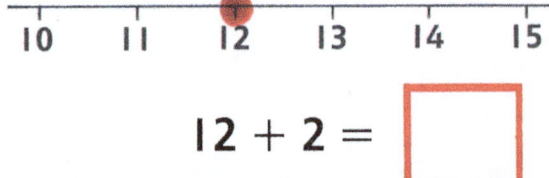 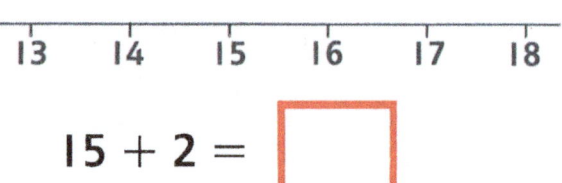

12 + 2 = ☐

15 + 2 = ☐

Complementary addition

Party food

20

Put more cherries on the cake.

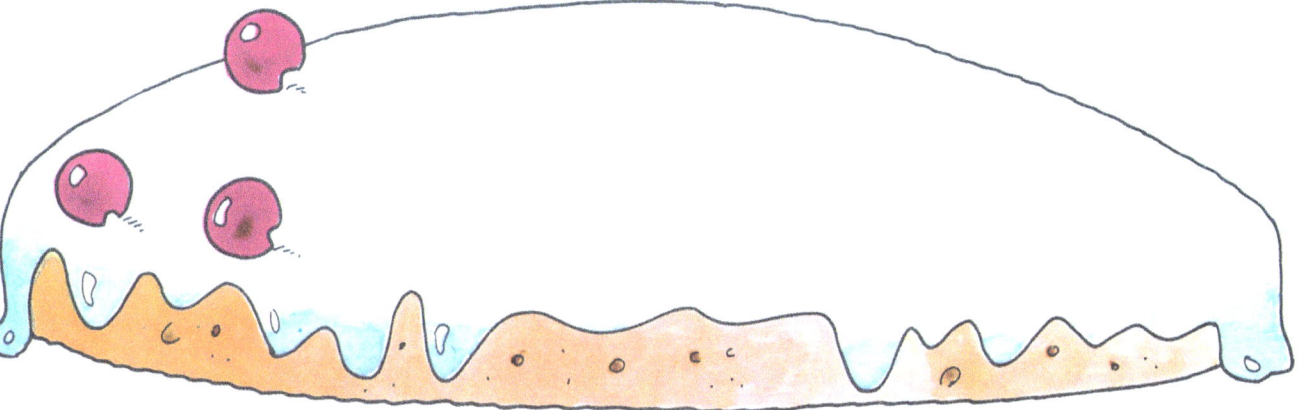

3 + ☐ = 5   3 + ☐ = 4

3 + ☐ = 6   3 + ☐ = 7

3 + ☐ = 9   3 + ☐ = 8

Draw more cakes.   Draw more cakes.

2 + ☐ = 5   5 + ☐ = 8

Draw more apples.   Draw more apples.

   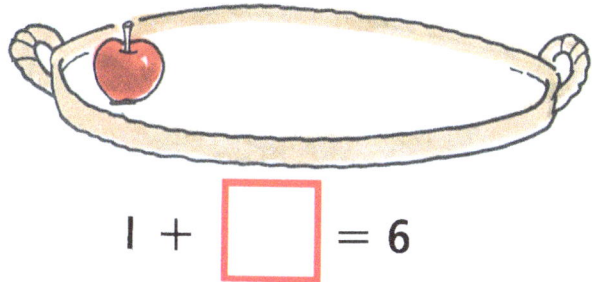

4 + ☐ = 7   1 + ☐ = 6

Complementary addition

Boats

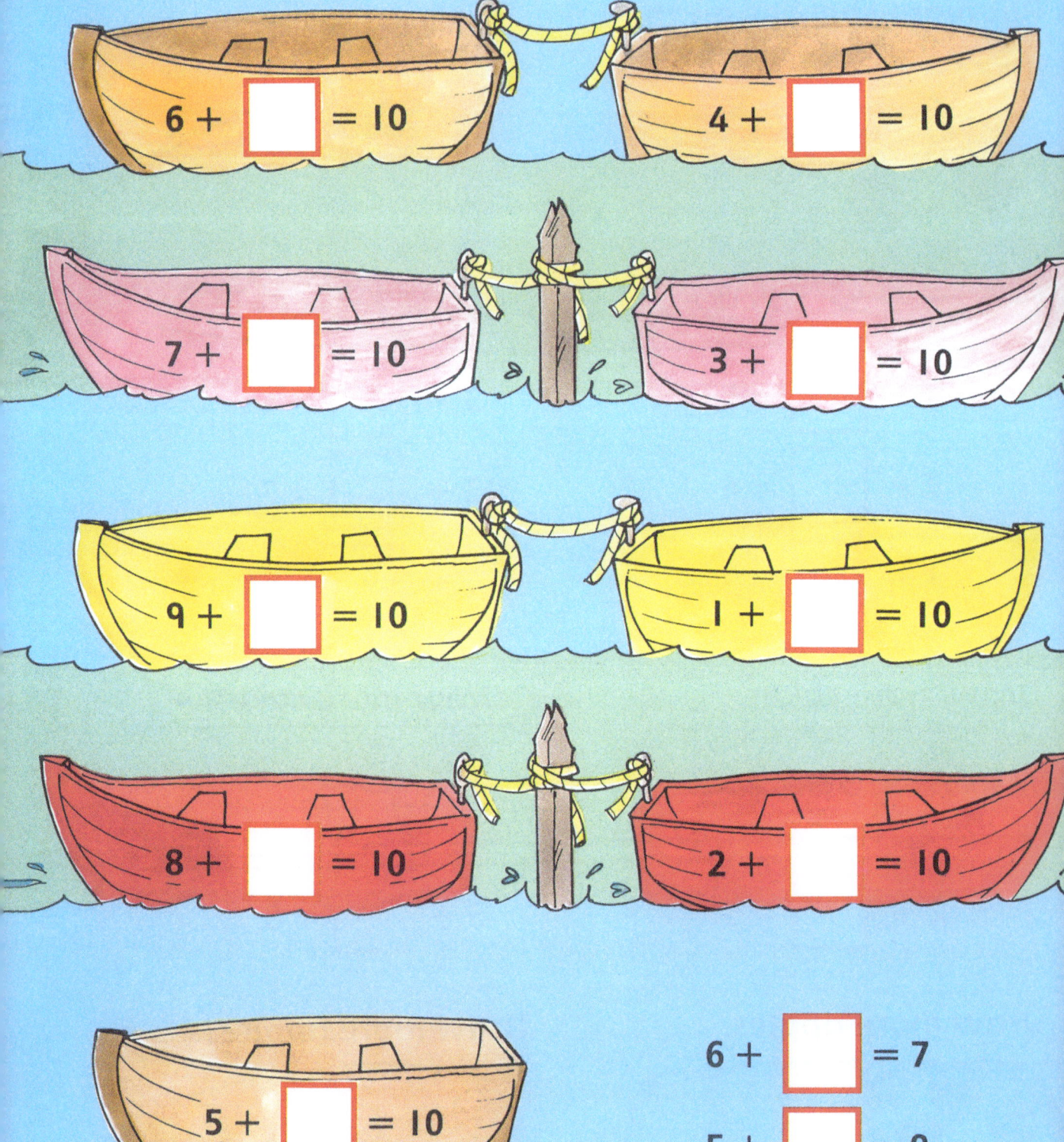

Difference in price

Vegetables

The difference in price is ☐ p.   6 − 4 =

You may use 🪙 coins.

Difference in price ☐ p   8 − 2 =

Difference in price ☐ p   9 − 6 =

Difference in price ☐ p

Difference in price ☐ p

Difference in price ☐ p

Plants

☐ plants

☐ plants

The difference between 9 and 6 is ___ .   9 − 6 = ☐

☐ trees

☐ trees

The difference between 4 and 8 is ___ .   8 − 4 = ☐

The difference between 7 and 5 is ___ .

☐ leaves   ☐ leaves

7 − 5 = ☐

The difference between 6 and 3 is ___ .

6 − 3 = ☐

The difference between 2 and 9 is ___ .

9 − 2 = ☐

1	2	3	4	5	6	7	8	9	10	11	12	13	14	15	16	17	18	19	20	21	22	23

Match the coins.

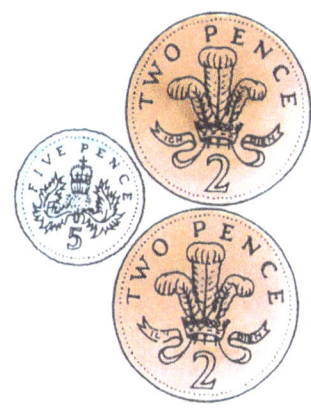

Problem solving

Colour **3** coins to buy a TOFFS.

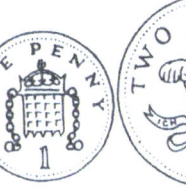

Ten pence

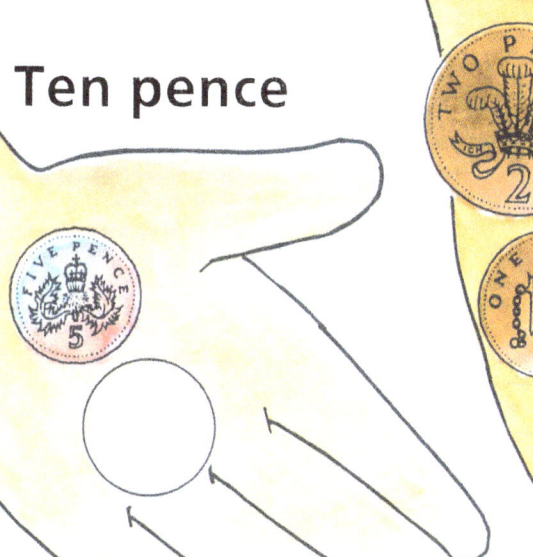

Put out coins. Make each set worth

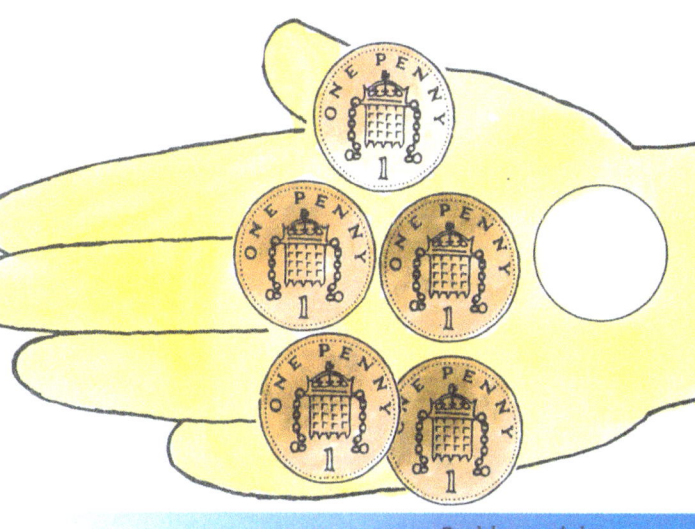

Problem solving

Colour coins to make 10p.

Problem solving

Buying things

Tom spends 10p altogether.
Write the price of the boat.

Lili spends 10p.
She buys two things.
Colour their labels.

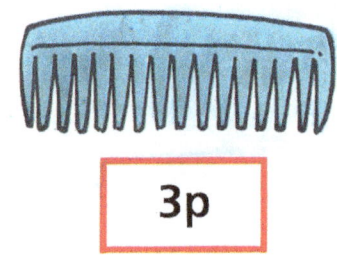

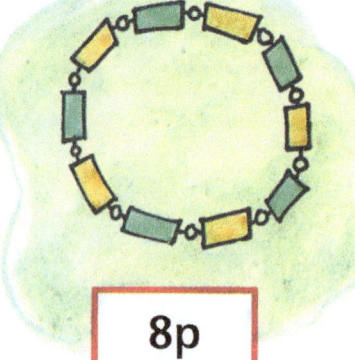

Buying stickers

Use coins. Put out the change.

Change from 5p

Change from 5p

Change from 10p

Change from 10p

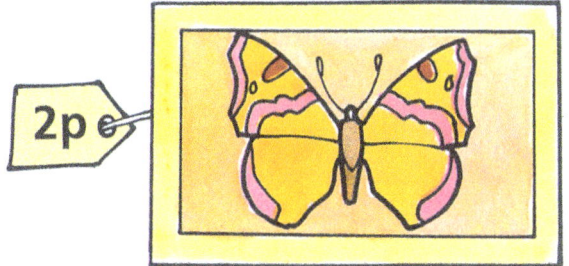

Change from 10p

show

Numbers to 20

8

| 11 | | 13 | 14 | 15 | 16 | 17 | | 19 | 20 |
| 11 | 12 | | | | | | 18 | | |

Write the number

after 13

after 19

after 17

before 17

before 11

before 20

15

Counting to 20

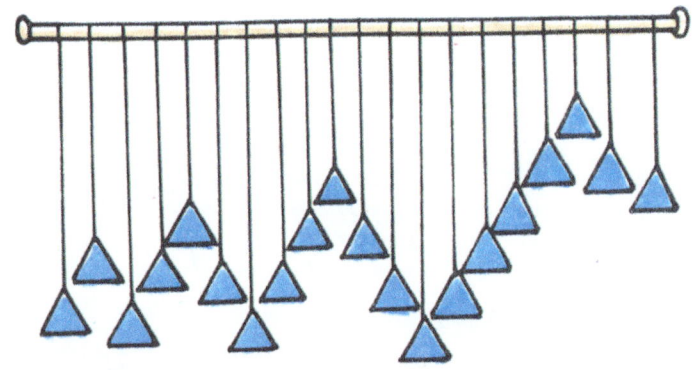

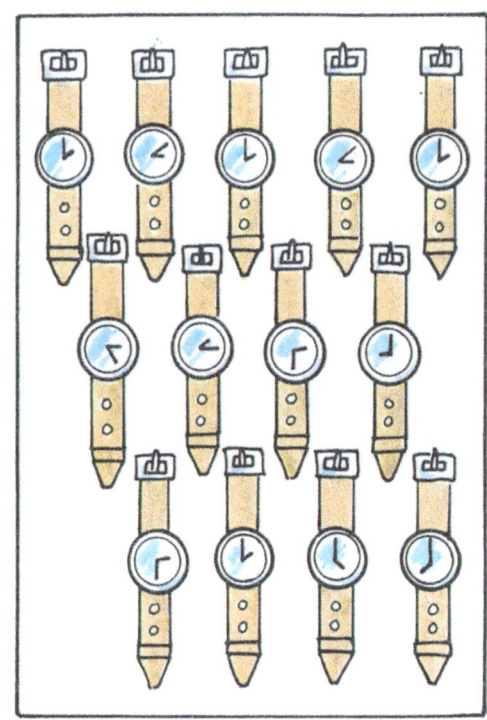

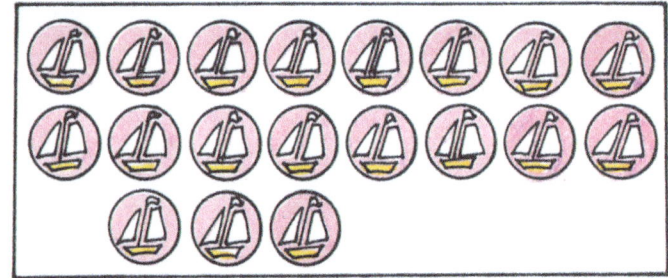

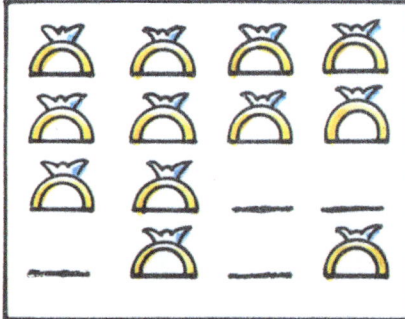

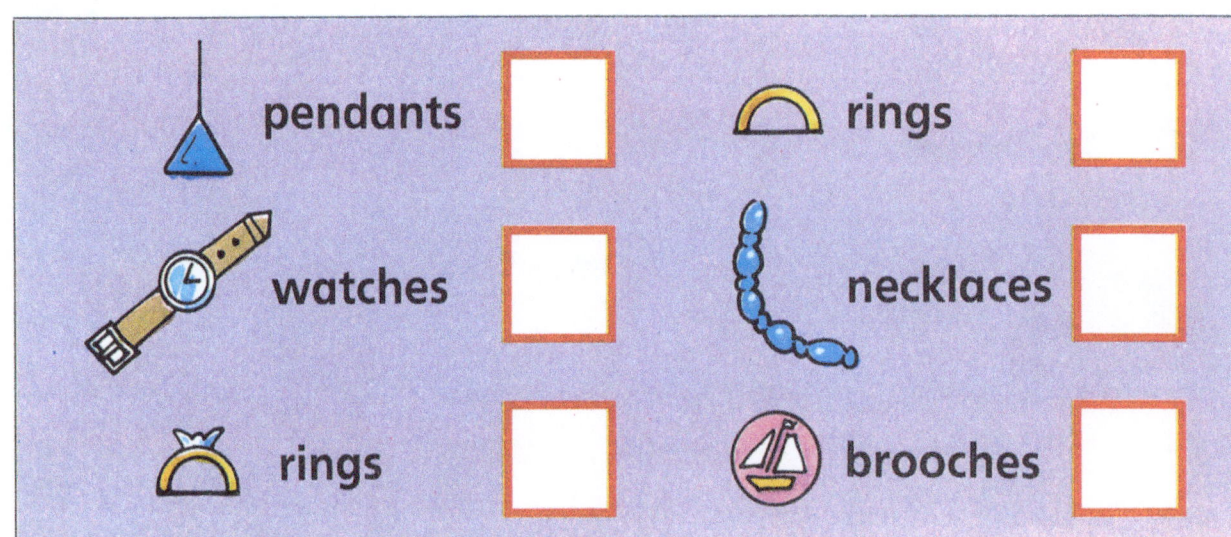

Jewellery shop

Counting to 20

10

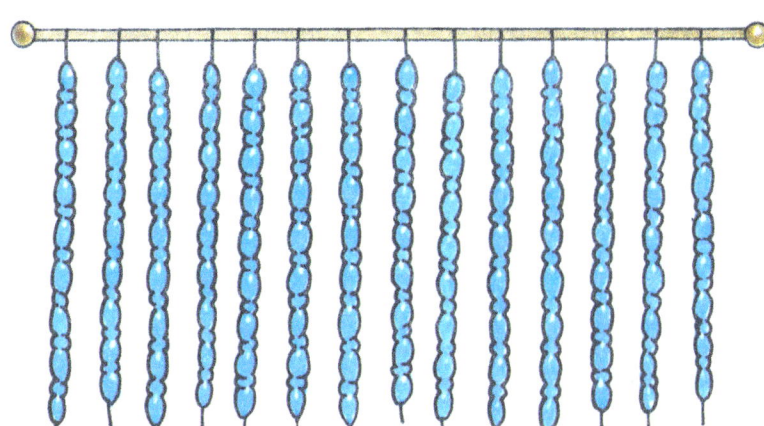
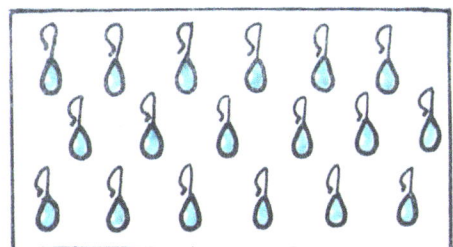

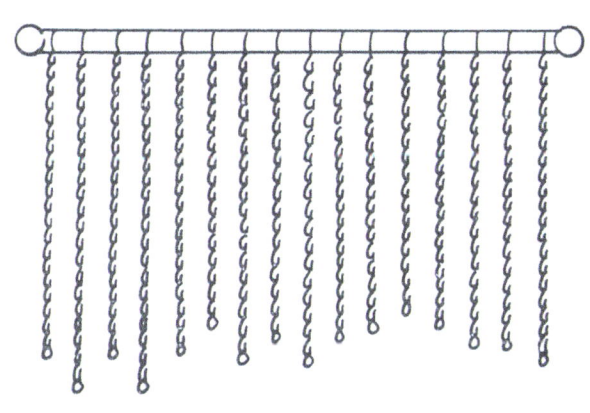
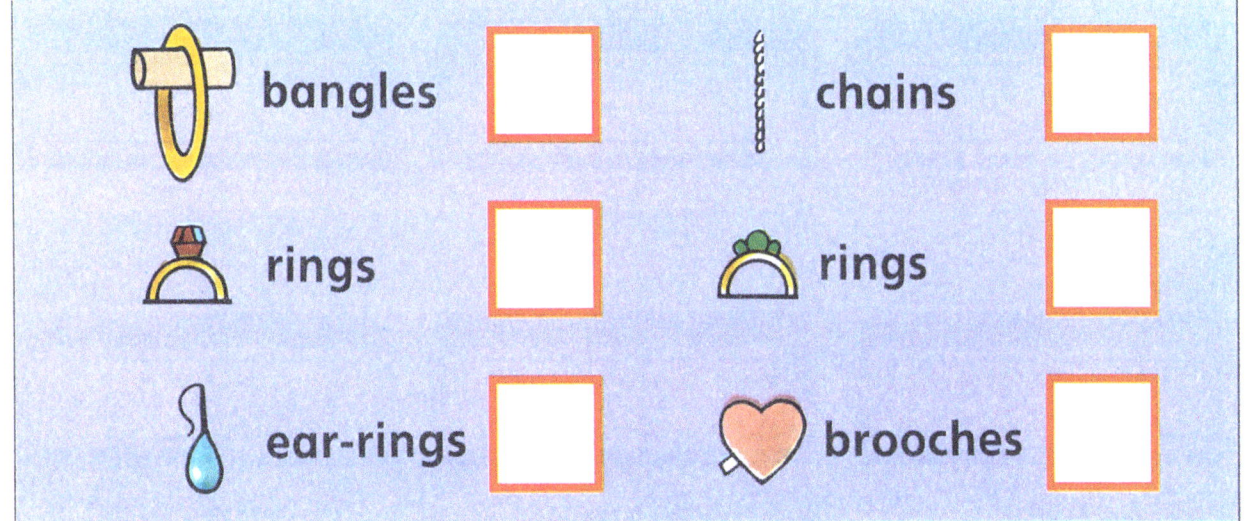

bangles		chains		
rings		rings		
ear-rings		brooches		

Number names to 20

Write the numbers.

Colour twenty red, twelve blue, thirteen yellow and

Use a calculator to show these numbers.
Write the numbers.

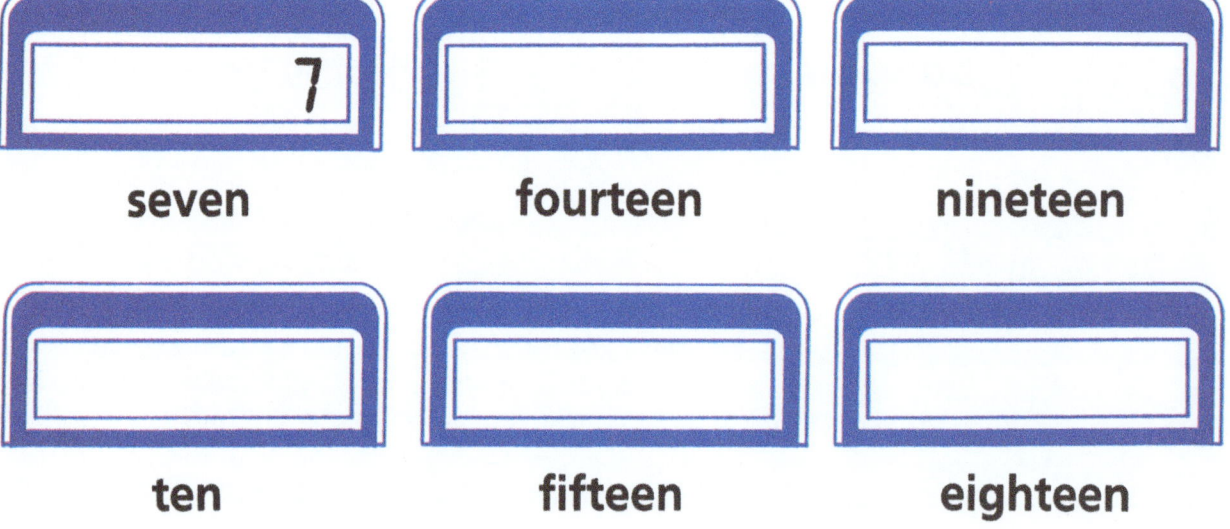

seven   fourteen   nineteen

ten   fifteen   eighteen

names

Number names to 20

| 12 |

- sixteen
- seventeen
- eighteen
- nineteen
- twenty

seventeen green.

Match

- nine
- eleven
- fourteen
- sixteen

The sunflower

Use cubes.

Count out 13.
Put 10 on the  .
13 = 10 and 3

Count out 19.
Put 10 on the   .
19 = 10 and ___

Count out 15.
Put 10 on the   .
15 = 10 and ___

Count out 18.
Put 10 on the  .
18 = 10 and ___

Count out 16.
Put 10 on the   .
16 = ___ and ___

Count out 12.
Put 10 on the   .
12 = ___ and ___

The beanstalk

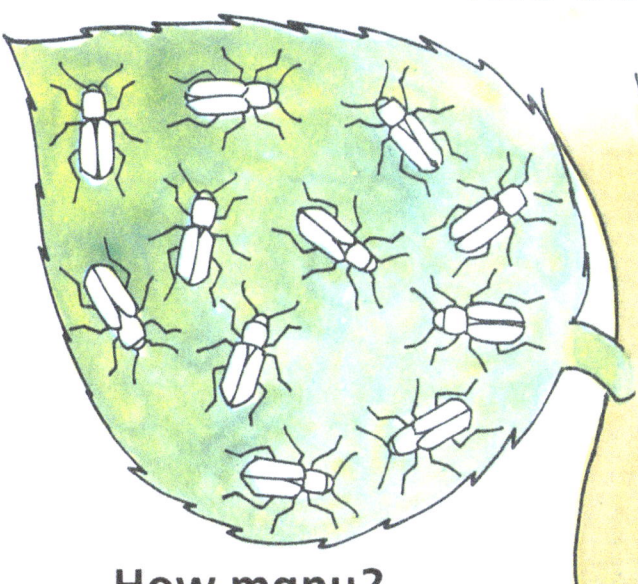

How many? ____
Colour 10 red.

11 = 10 + ____

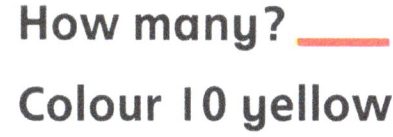

How many? ____
Colour 10 yellow.

14 = 10 + ____

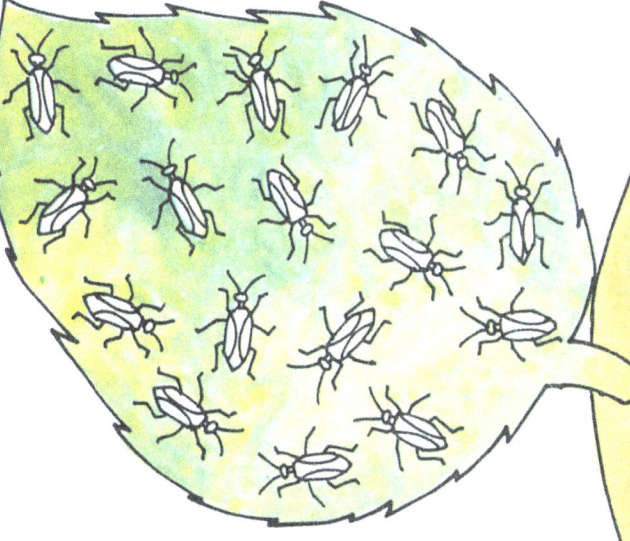

How many? ____
Colour 10 blue.

17 = ____ + ____

How many? ____
Colour 10 purple.

15 = ____ + ____

19 = ____ + ____

12 = ____ + ____

16 = ____ + ____

The garden centre

10 + ___

How many altogether? ☐

10 + ___

How many altogether? ☐

10 + ___

How many altogether? ☐

10 + ___

How many altogether? ☐

10 + ___

How many altogether? ☐

10 + ___

How many altogether? ☐

Loading bricks

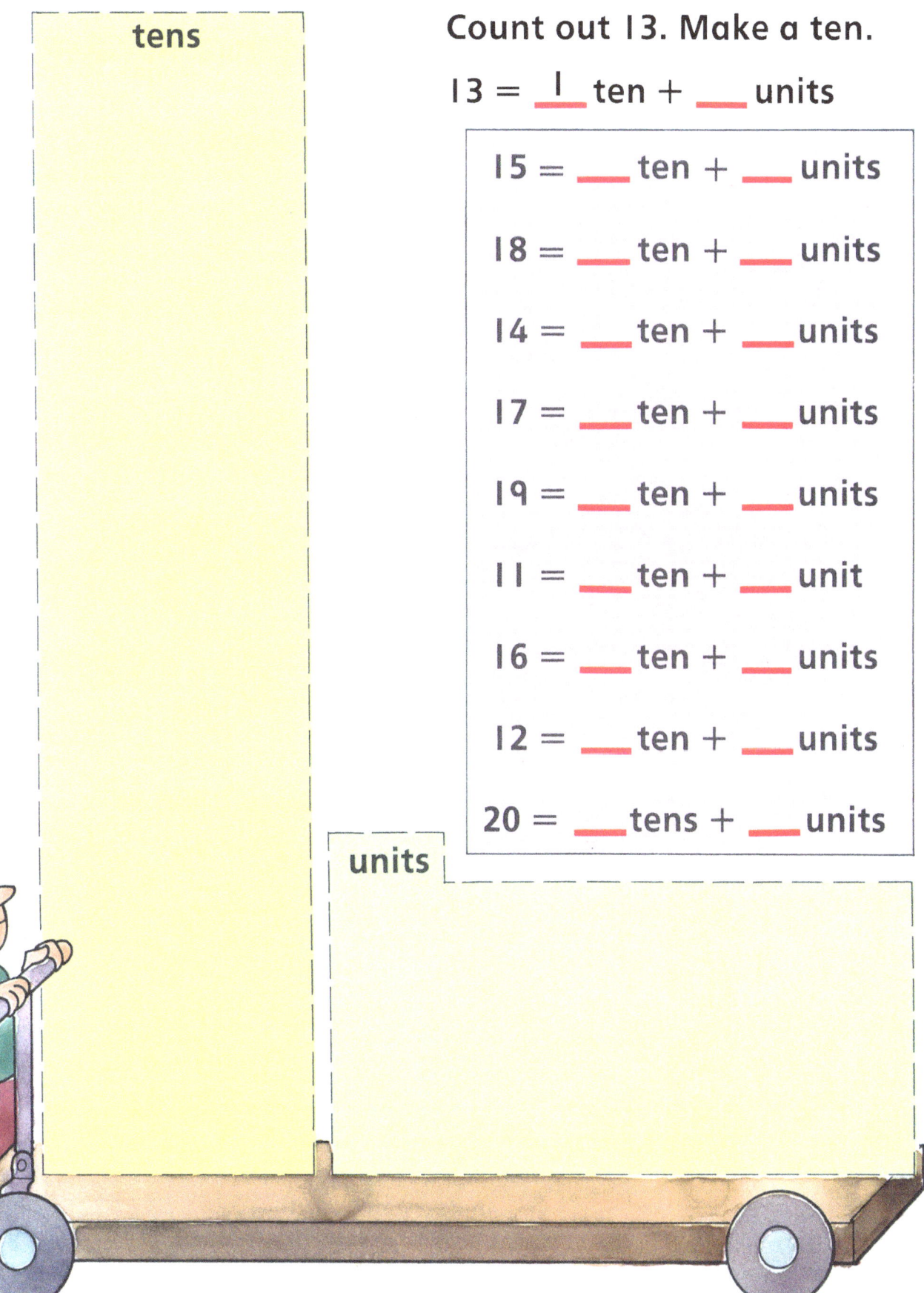

Count out 13. Make a ten.

13 = __1__ ten + ____ units

15 = ____ ten + ____ units

18 = ____ ten + ____ units

14 = ____ ten + ____ units

17 = ____ ten + ____ units

19 = ____ ten + ____ units

11 = ____ ten + ____ unit

16 = ____ ten + ____ units

12 = ____ ten + ____ units

20 = ____ tens + ____ units

Place value to 20

More bricks

tens

Put out 1 ten and 5 units.
How many cubes altogether? ☐

1 ten + 5 units = ☐

1 ten + 2 units = ☐

1 ten + 7 units = ☐

1 ten + 4 units = ☐

1 ten + 1 unit = ☐

1 ten + 6 units = ☐

2 tens + 0 units = ☐

units

Cranes

Colour the boxes to match the cranes.

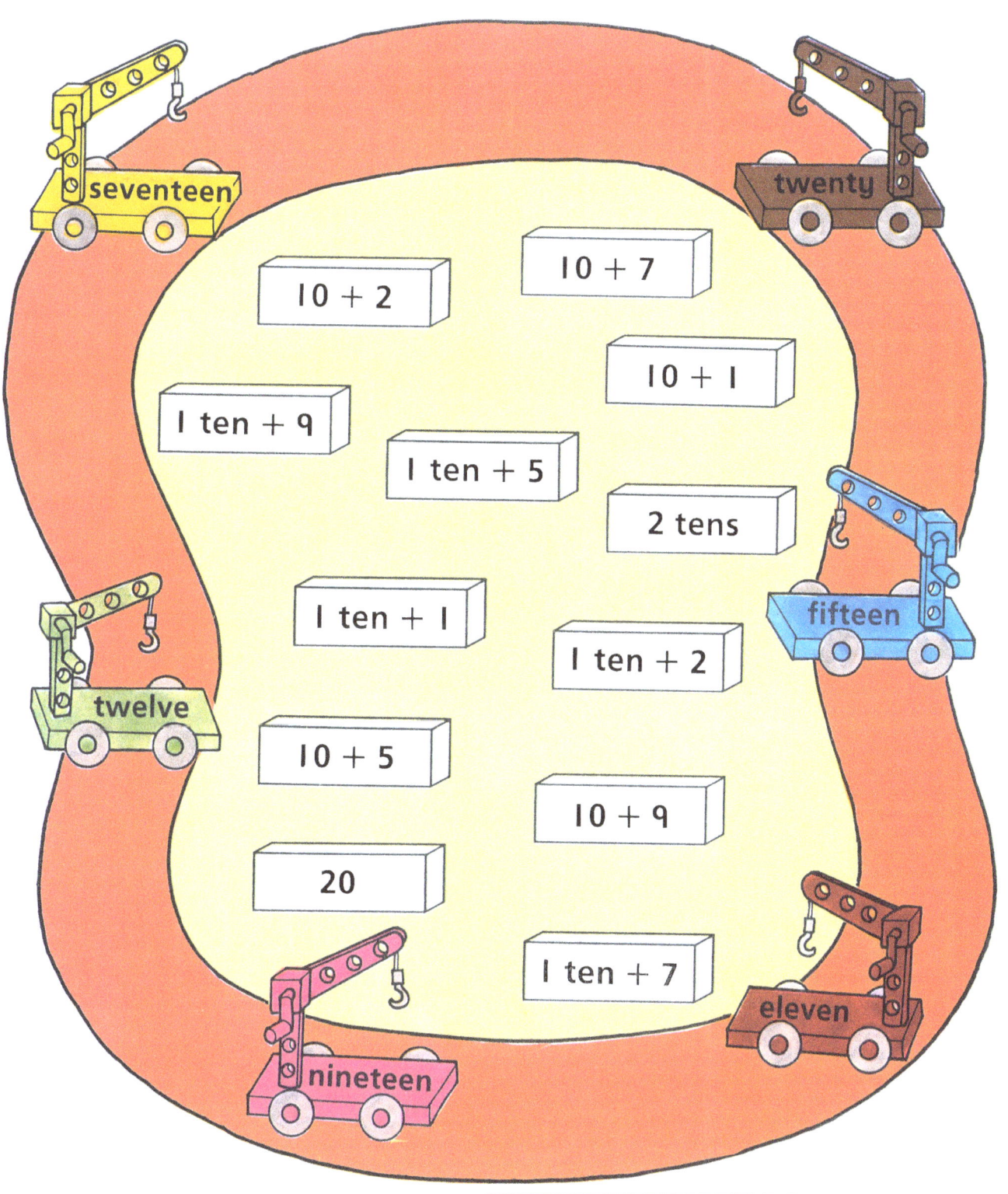

Bunny hops

Start at 4.   Count on 3.   4 + 3 = ☐

Start at 8.   Count on 3.   8 + 3 = ☐

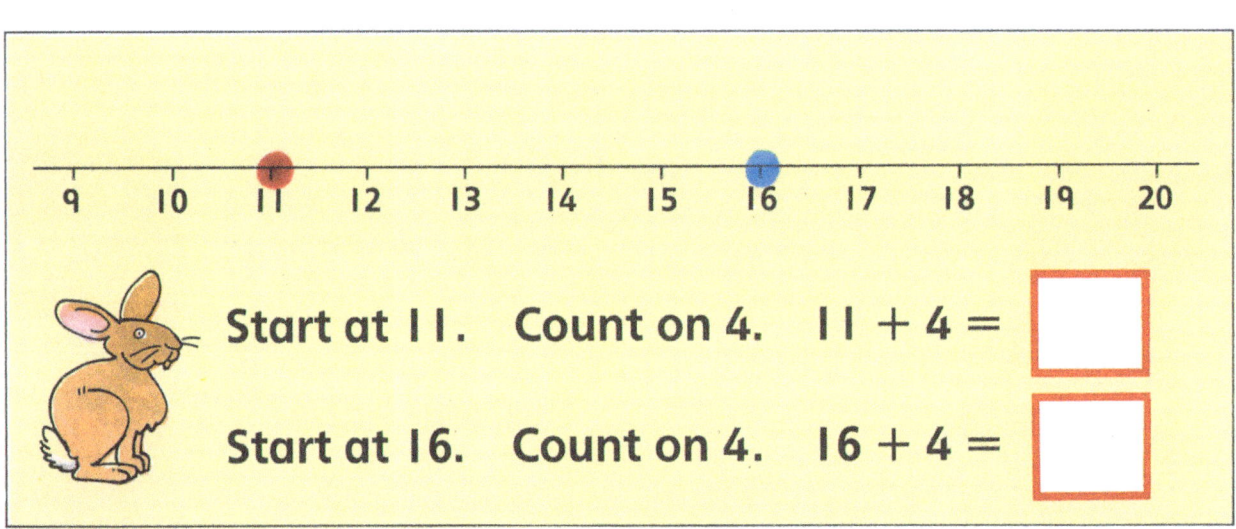

Start at 11.   Count on 4.   11 + 4 = ☐

Start at 16.   Count on 4.   16 + 4 = ☐

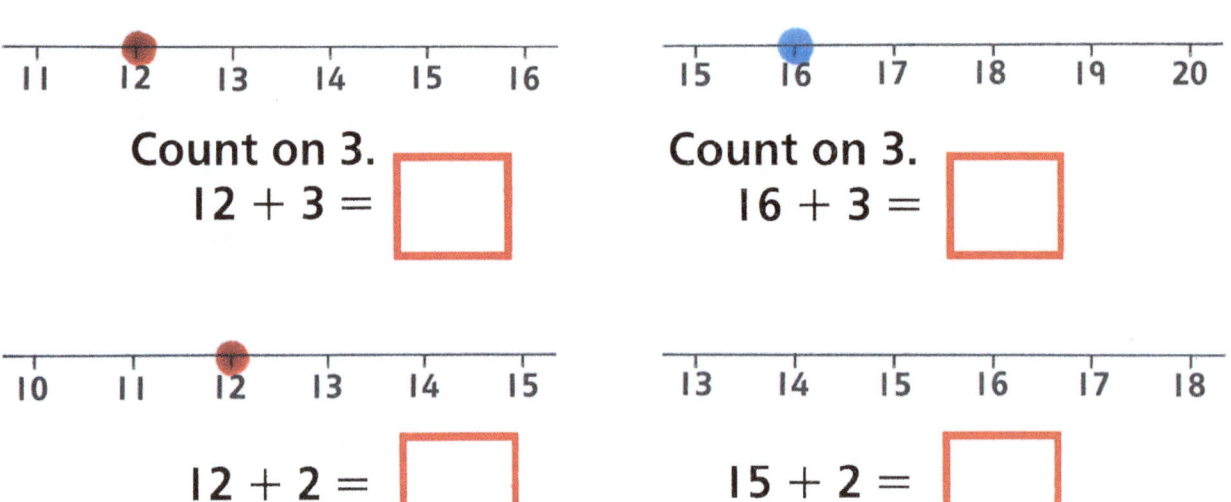

Count on 3.
12 + 3 = ☐

Count on 3.
16 + 3 = ☐

12 + 2 = ☐

15 + 2 = ☐

Complementary addition

Party food

20

Put more cherries on the cake.

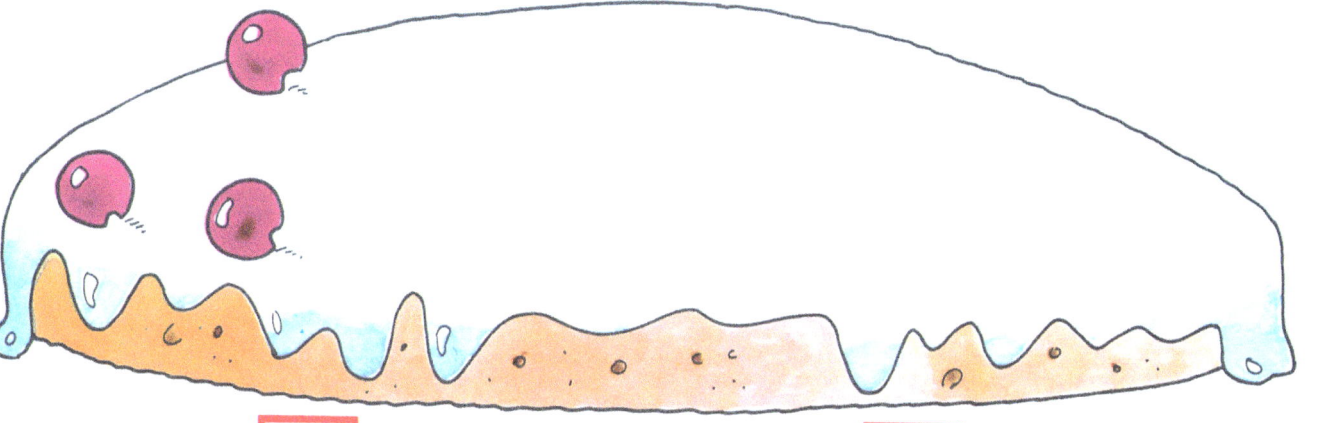

3 + ☐ = 5   3 + ☐ = 4

3 + ☐ = 6   3 + ☐ = 7

3 + ☐ = 9   3 + ☐ = 8

Draw more cakes.   Draw more cakes.

2 + ☐ = 5   5 + ☐ = 8

Draw more apples.   Draw more apples.

   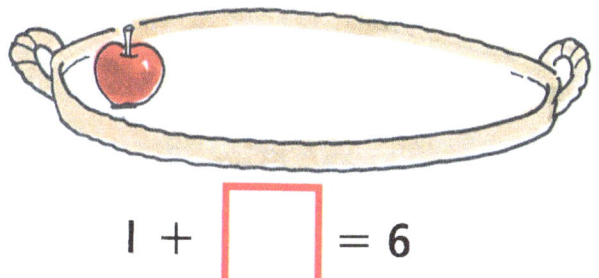

4 + ☐ = 7   1 + ☐ = 6

Complementary addition

Boats

6 + ☐ = 10   4 + ☐ = 10

7 + ☐ = 10   3 + ☐ = 10

9 + ☐ = 10   1 + ☐ = 10

8 + ☐ = 10   2 + ☐ = 10

5 + ☐ = 10

6 + ☐ = 7
5 + ☐ = 9
4 + ☐ = 6

Difference in price

Vegetables

The difference in price is ☐ p.   6 − 4 =

You may use 🪙 coins.

  Difference in price ☐ p   8 − 2 =

  Difference in price ☐ p   9 − 6 =

  Difference in price ☐ p

 Difference in price ☐ p

 Difference in price ☐ p

Plants

☐ plants

☐ plants

The difference between 9 and 6 is ___.   9 − 6 = ☐

☐ trees

☐ trees

The difference between 4 and 8 is ___.   8 − 4 = ☐

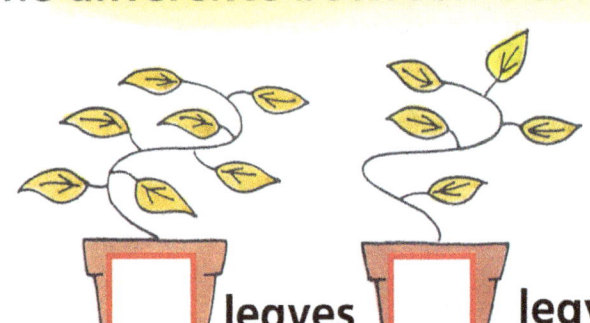

☐ leaves   ☐ leaves

The difference between 7 and 5 is ___.

7 − 5 = ☐

The difference between 6 and 3 is ___.

6 − 3 = ☐

The difference between 2 and 9 is ___.

9 − 2 = ☐

1	2	3	4	5	6	7	8	9	10	11	12	13	14	15	16	17	18	19	20	21	22	23

Money to 9p

2

Match the coins.

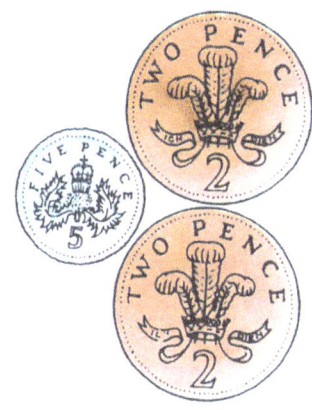

Problem solving

Colour **3** coins to buy a .

 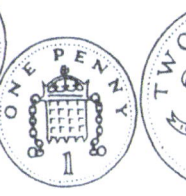     

Ten pence

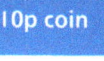
10p coin

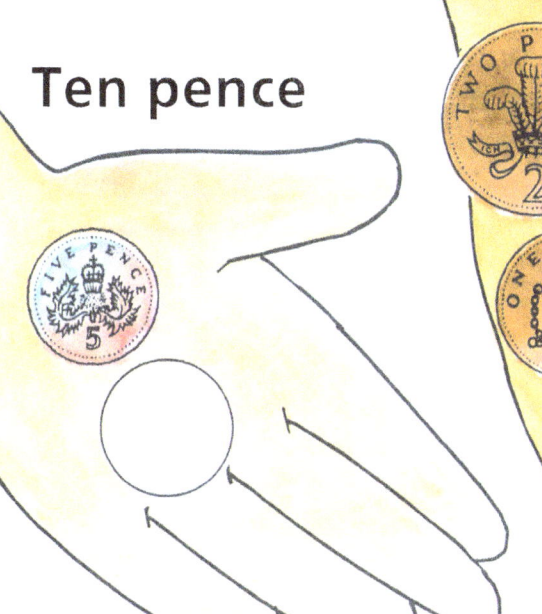

Put out coins.
Make each set worth 10p.

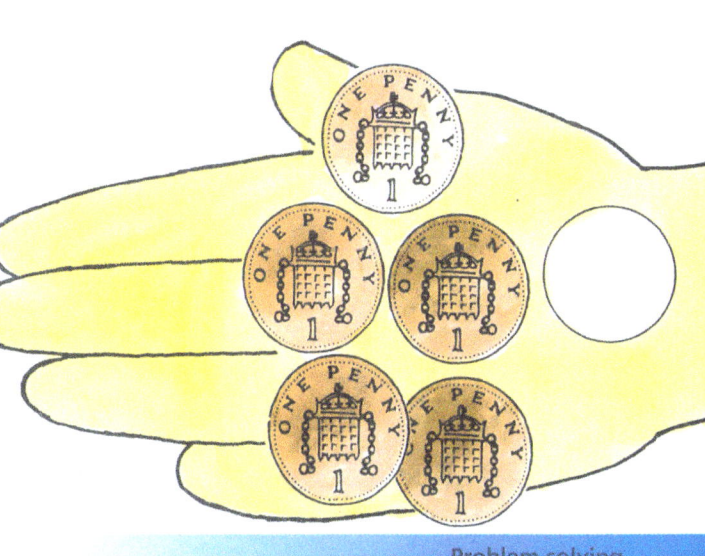

Problem solving

Colour coins to make 10p.

Problem solving

Buying things

Tom spends 10p altogether.
Write the price of the boat.

3p   2p

Lili spends 10p.
She buys two things.
Colour their labels.

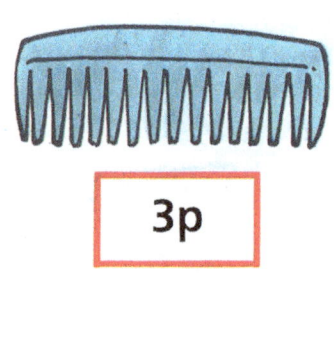

3p

6p

4p

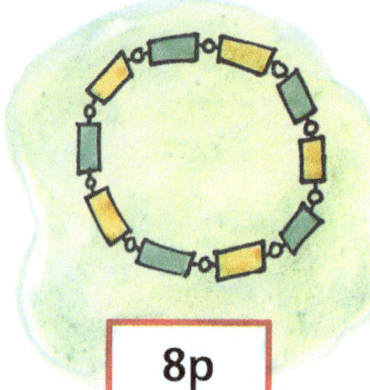

8p

7p

Buying stickers

Use coins. Put out the change.

R6

2p

Change from 5p

1p

Change from 5p

7p

Change from 10p

4p

Change from 10p

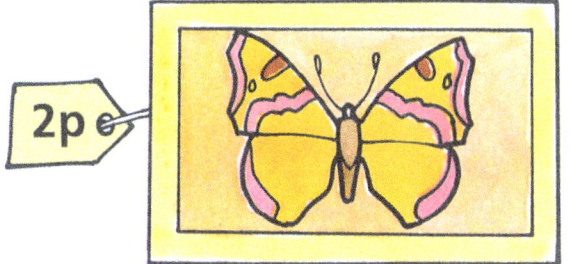
2p

Change from 10p

show

Numbers to 20

8

Write the number

after 13

after 19

after 17

before 17

before 11

before 20

Counting to 20

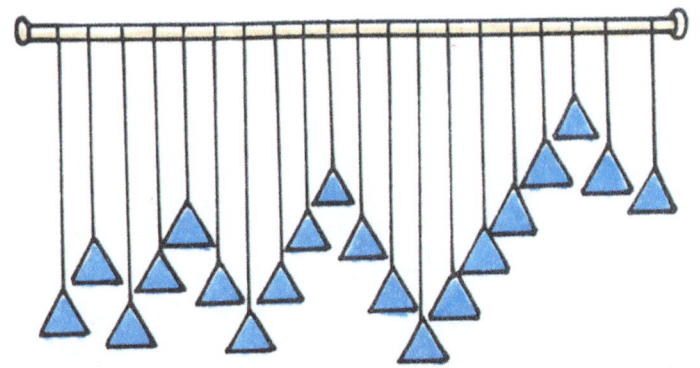
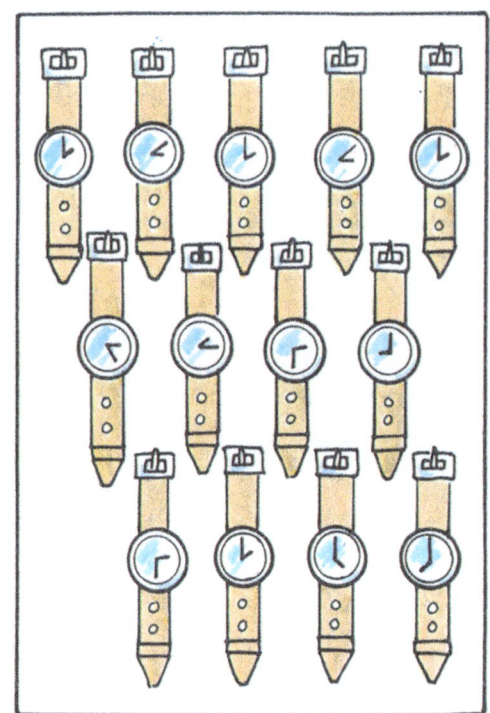

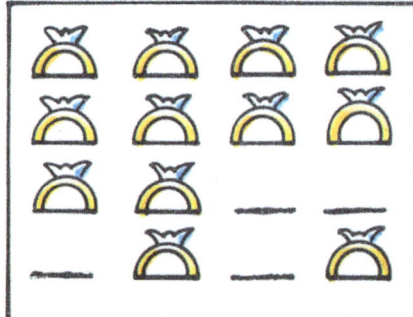

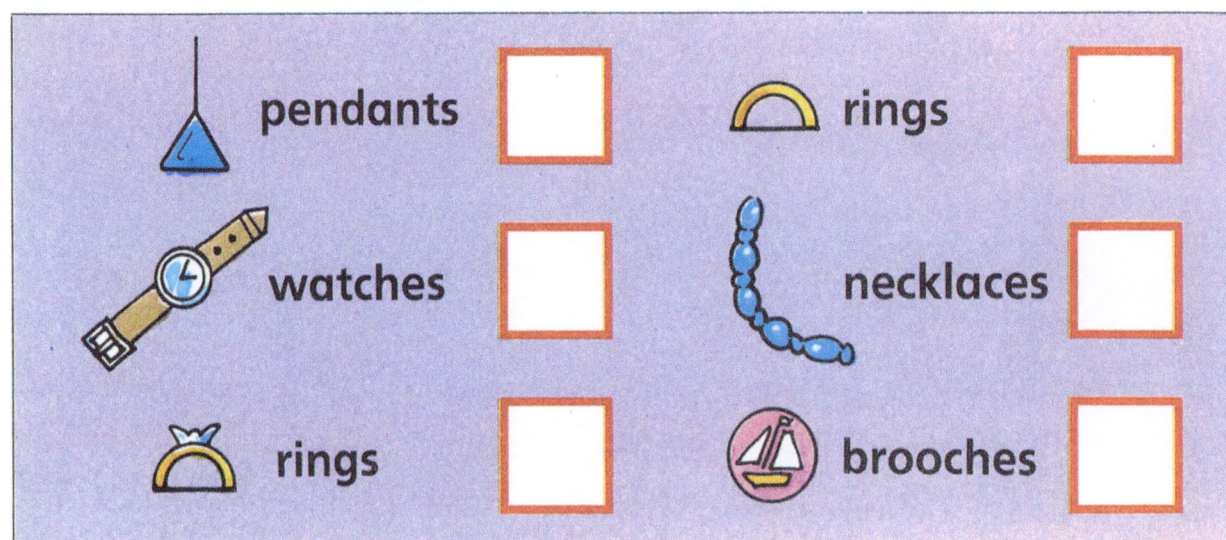

Jewellery shop

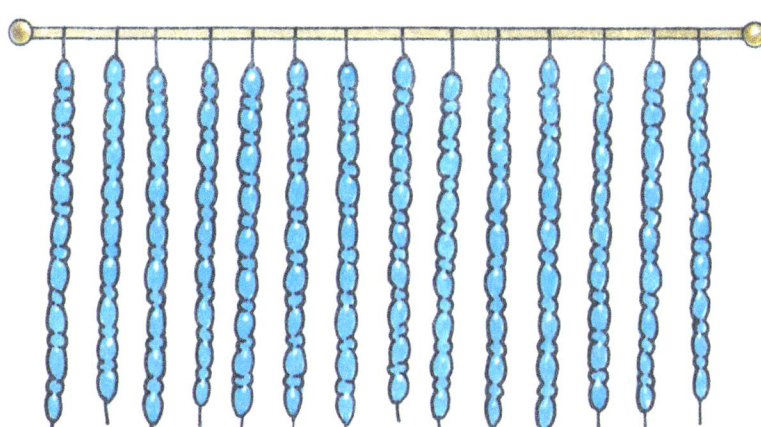
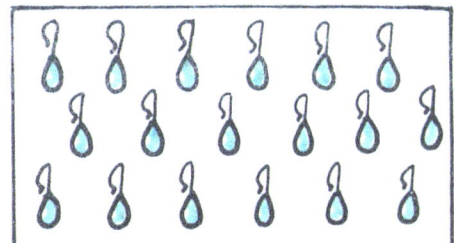
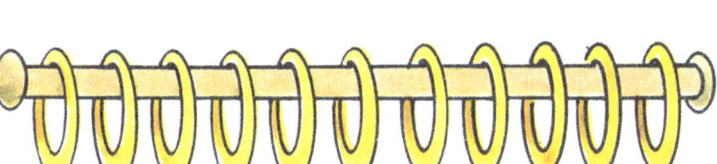
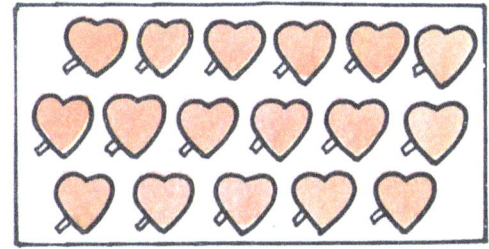

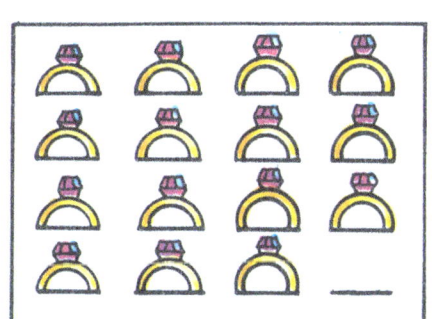
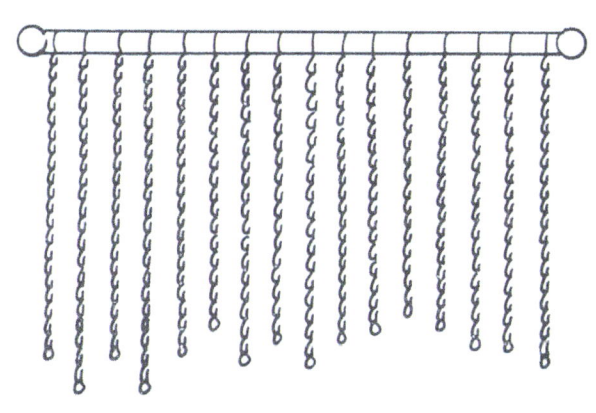
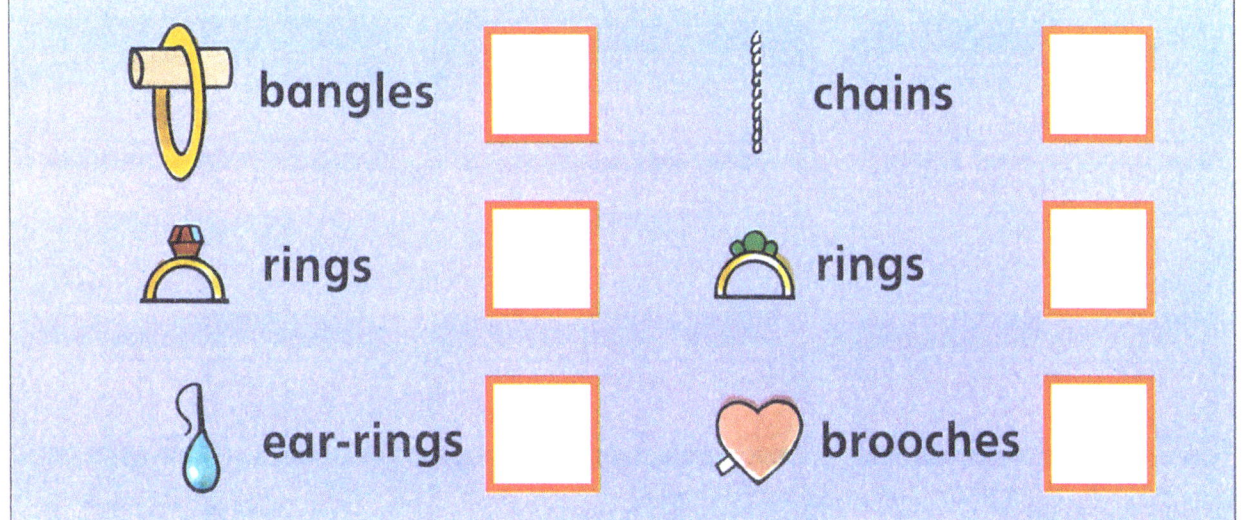

Number names to 20

Write the numbers.

Colour twenty red, twelve blue, thirteen yellow and

Use a calculator to show these numbers.
Write the numbers.

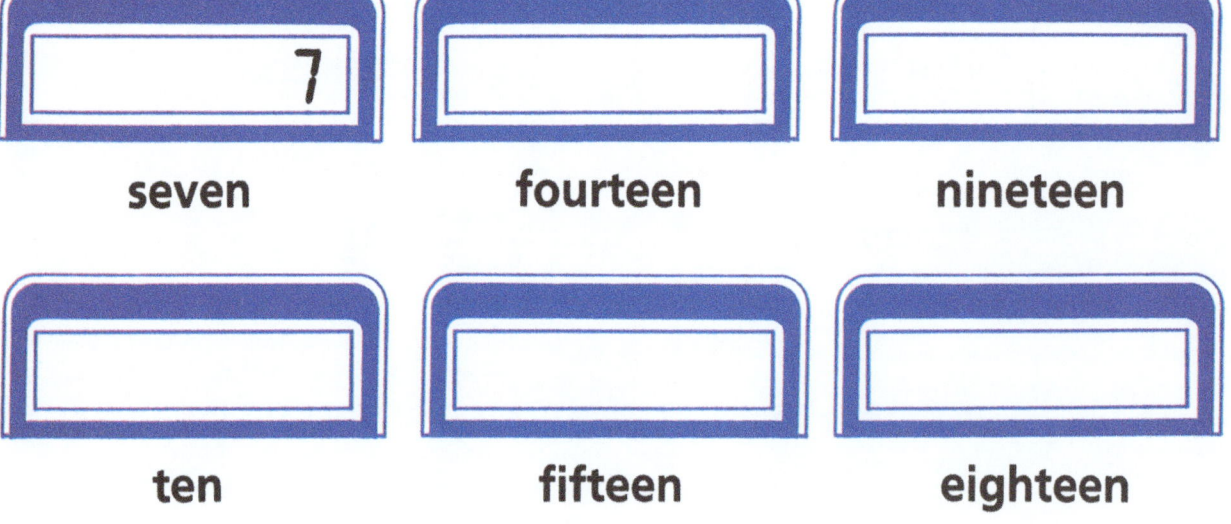

seven   fourteen   nineteen

ten   fifteen   eighteen

names

Number names to 20

12

sixteen seventeen eighteen nineteen twenty

seventeen green.

Match

nine
eleven
fourteen
sixteen

Towards place value

The sunflower

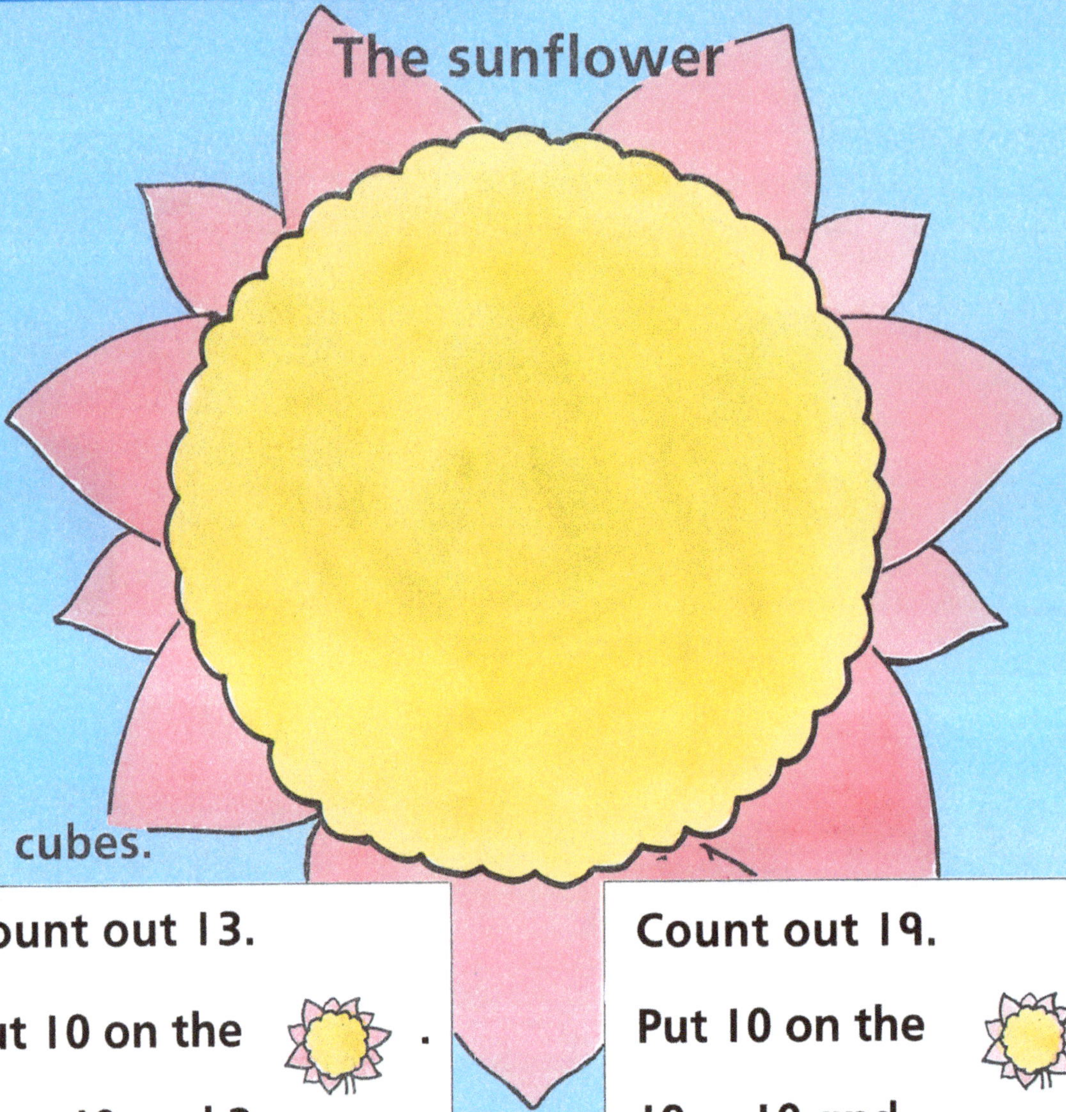

Use cubes.

Count out 13.
Put 10 on the  .
13 = 10 and 3

Count out 19.
Put 10 on the  .
19 = 10 and ___

Count out 15.
Put 10 on the  .
15 = 10 and ___

Count out 18.
Put 10 on the  .
18 = 10 and ___

Count out 16.
Put 10 on the   .
16 = ___ and ___

Count out 12.
Put 10 on the  .
12 = ___ and ___

The beanstalk

Towards place value

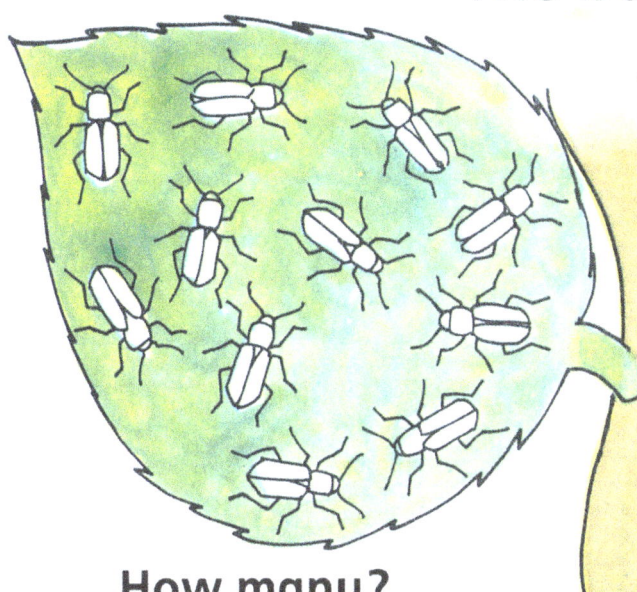

How many? ____
Colour 10 red.

11 = 10 + ____

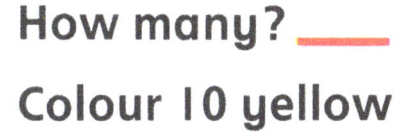

How many? ____
Colour 10 yellow.

14 = 10 + ____

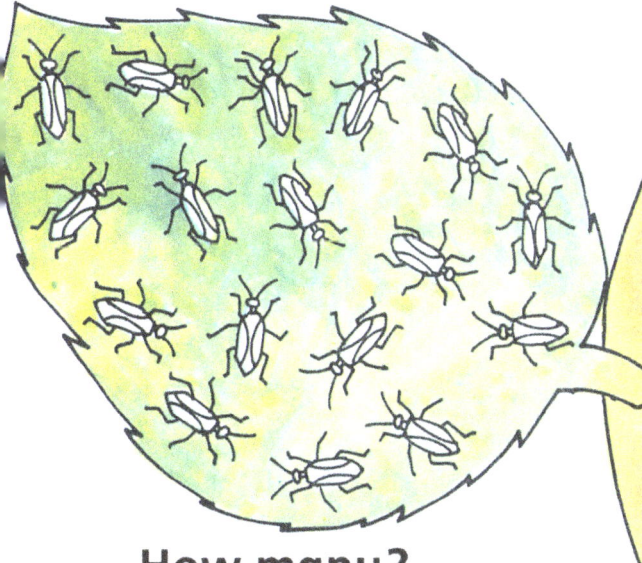

How many? ____
Colour 10 blue.

17 = ____ + ____

How many? ____
Colour 10 purple.

15 = ____ + ____

19 = ____ + ____
12 = ____ + ____
16 = ____ + ____

The garden centre

10 + ___

How many altogether? ☐

10 + ___

How many altogether?

10 + ___

How many altogether? ☐

10 + ___

How many altogether?

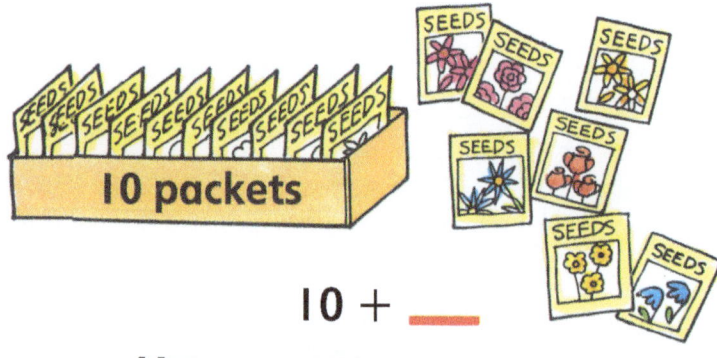

10 + ___

How many altogether? ☐

10 + ___

How many altogether?

Loading bricks

Count out 13. Make a ten.

13 = __1__ ten + ____ units

15 = ____ ten + ____ units

18 = ____ ten + ____ units

14 = ____ ten + ____ units

17 = ____ ten + ____ units

19 = ____ ten + ____ units

11 = ____ ten + ____ unit

16 = ____ ten + ____ units

12 = ____ ten + ____ units

20 = ____ tens + ____ units

Place value to 20

More bricks

Put out 1 ten and 5 units.
How many cubes altogether? ☐

1 ten + 5 units = ☐

1 ten + 2 units = ☐

1 ten + 7 units = ☐

1 ten + 4 units = ☐

1 ten + 1 unit = ☐

1 ten + 6 units = ☐

2 tens + 0 units = ☐

tens

units

Cranes

Colour the boxes to match the cranes.

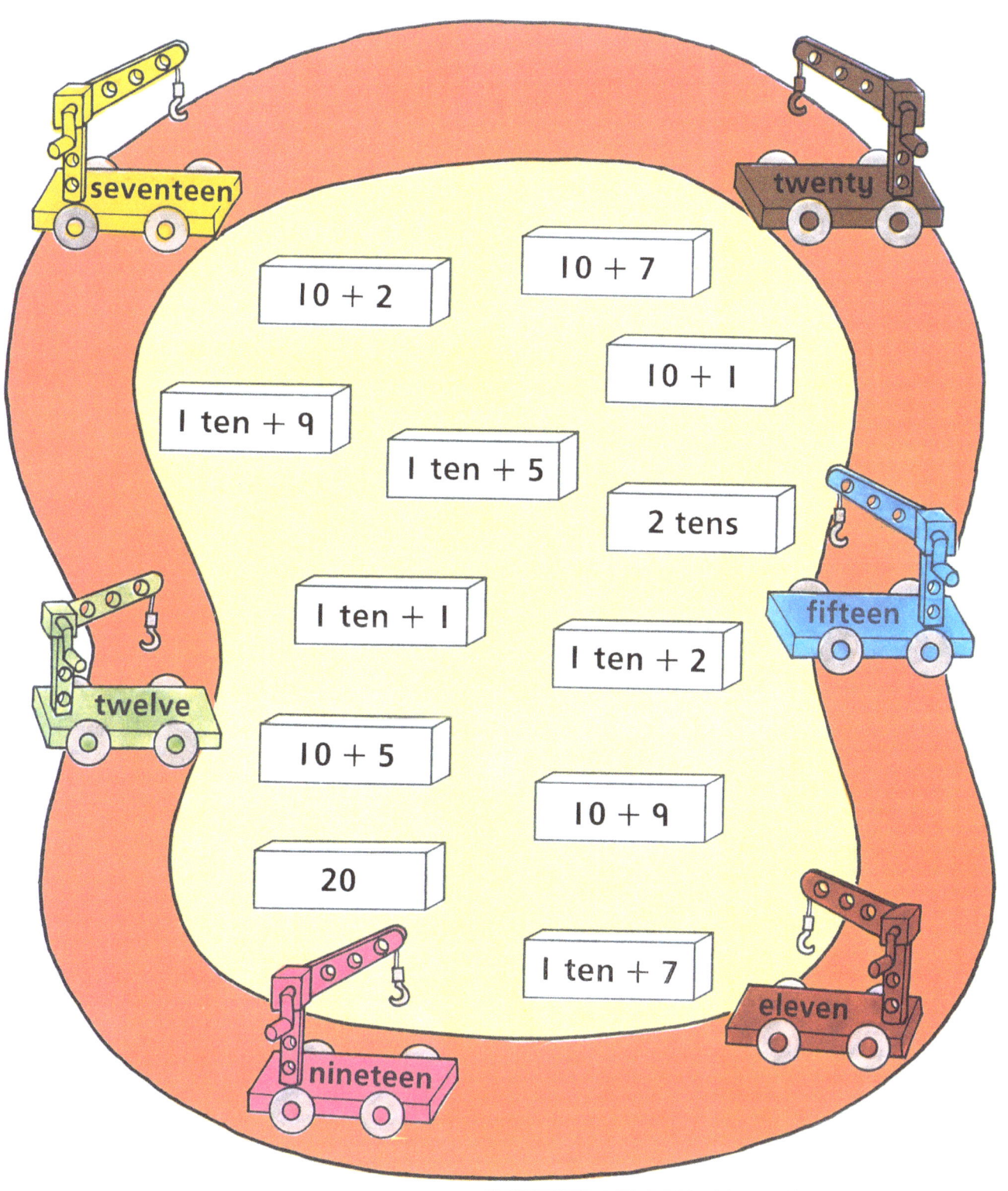

Bunny hops

Start at 4. Count on 3. 4 + 3 =

Start at 8. Count on 3. 8 + 3 =

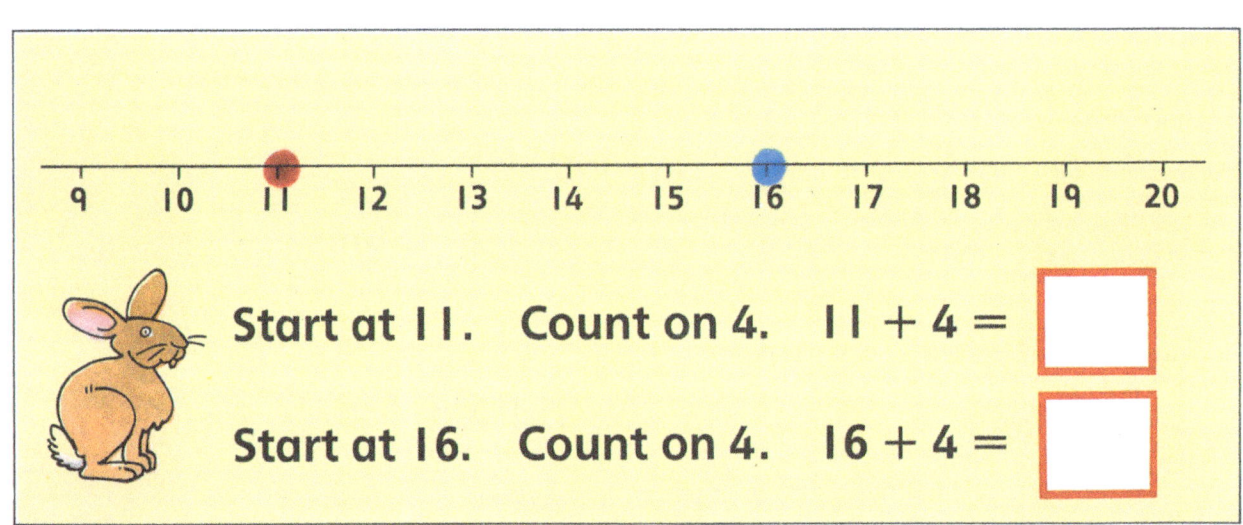

Start at 11. Count on 4. 11 + 4 =

Start at 16. Count on 4. 16 + 4 =

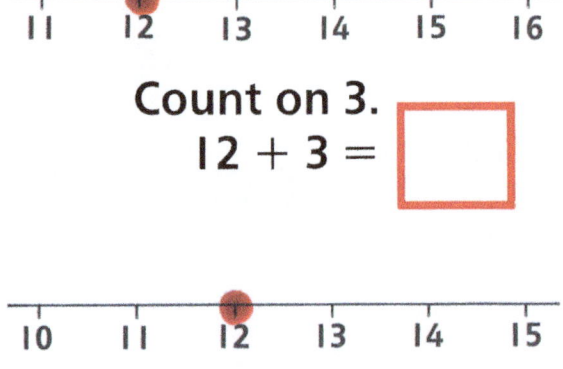

Count on 3.
12 + 3 =

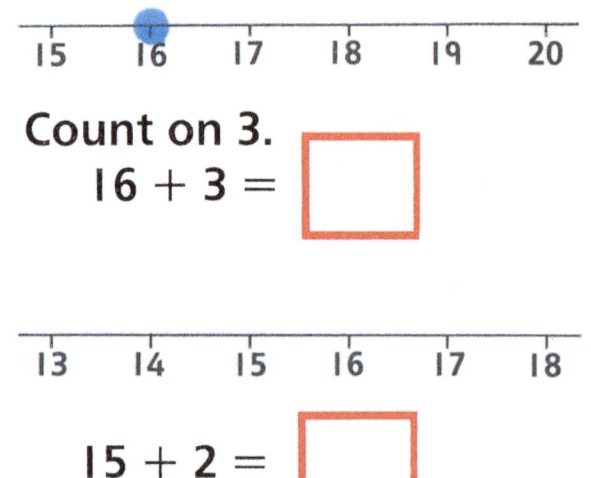

Count on 3.
16 + 3 =

12 + 2 =

15 + 2 =

Party food

Put more cherries on the cake.

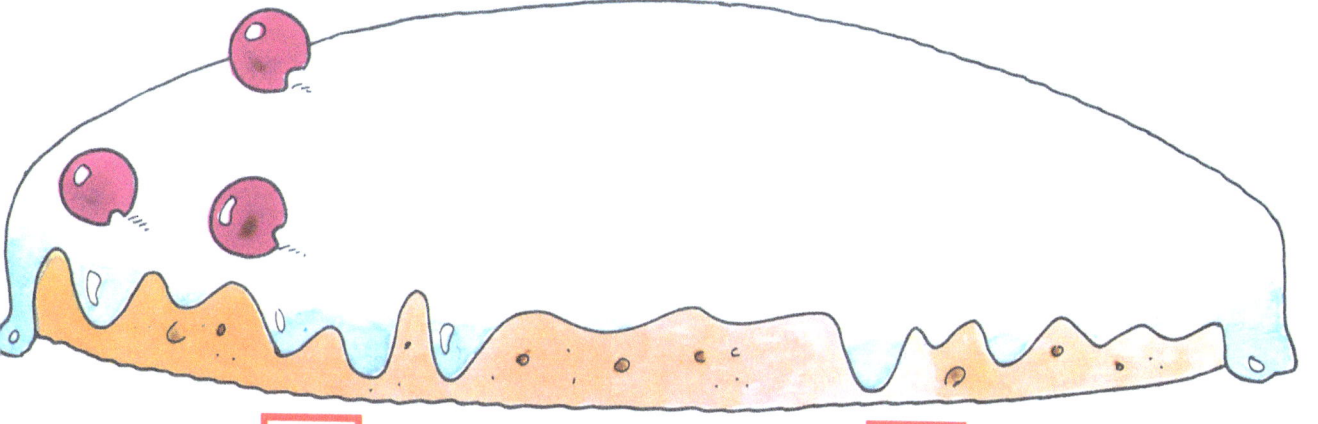

3 + ☐ = 5   3 + ☐ = 4

3 + ☐ = 6   3 + ☐ = 7

3 + ☐ = 9   3 + ☐ = 8

Draw more cakes.   Draw more cakes.

2 + ☐ = 5   5 + ☐ = 8

Draw more apples.   Draw more apples.

   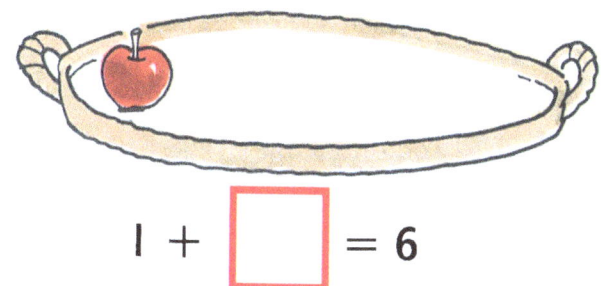

4 + ☐ = 7   1 + ☐ = 6

Vegetables

The difference in price is ☐ p.   6 − 4 =

You may use  coins.

  Difference in price ☐ p   8 − 2 =

  Difference in price ☐ p   9 − 6 =

  Difference in price ☐ p

 Difference in price ☐ p

 Difference in price ☐ p

Plants

☐ plants

☐ plants

The difference between 9 and 6 is ___ .   9 − 6 = ☐

☐ trees

☐ trees

The difference between 4 and 8 is ___ .   8 − 4 = ☐

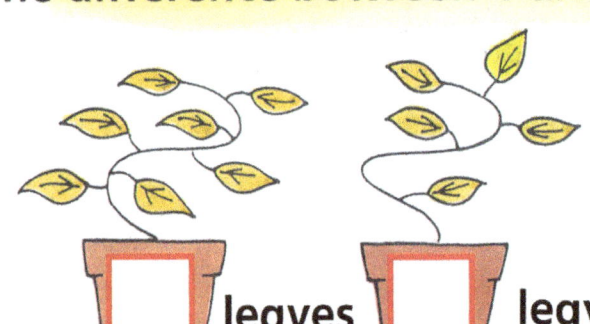

The difference between 7 and 5 is ___ .

☐ leaves   ☐ leaves

7 − 5 = ☐

The difference between 6 and 3 is ___ .

The difference between 2 and 9 is ___ .

6 − 3 = ☐

9 − 2 = ☐

Match the coins.

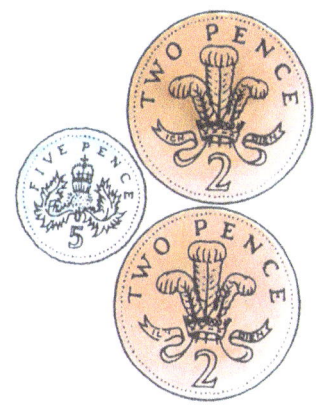

Problem solving

Colour **3** coins to buy a TOFFS.

Ten pence

10p coin

4

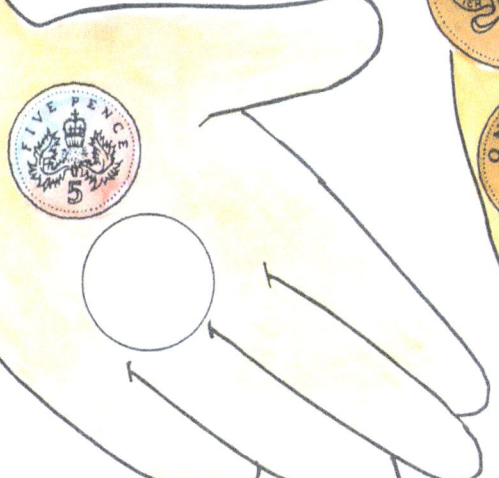

Put out coins.
Make each set worth

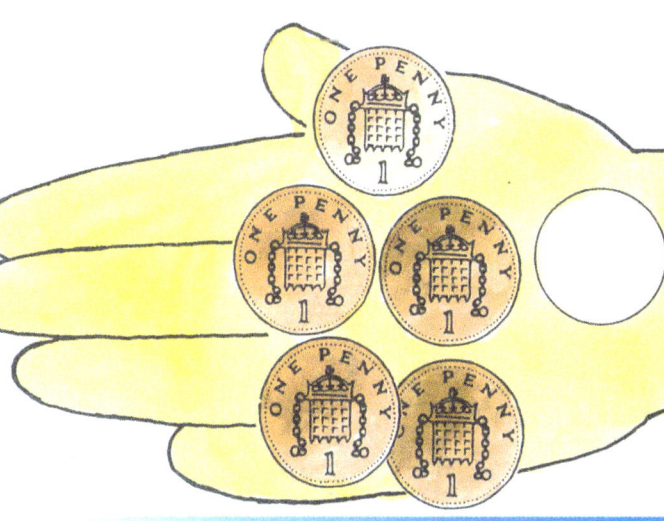

Problem solving

Colour coins to make 10p.

Problem solving

Buying things

Tom spends 10p altogether.
Write the price of the boat.

3p   2p

Lili spends 10p.
She buys two things.
Colour their labels.

3p

6p

4p

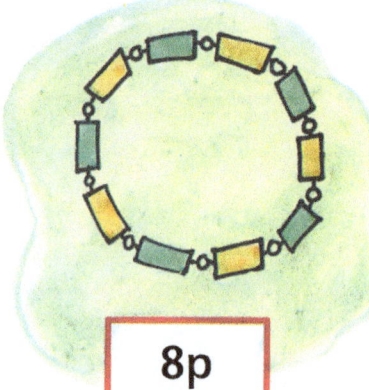

8p

7p

Buying stickers

Use coins. Put out the change.

Change from 5p

Change from 5p

Change from 10p

Change from 10p

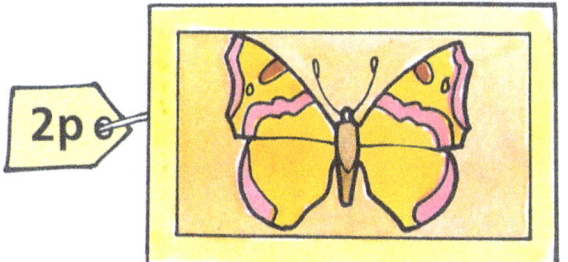

Change from 10p

show

Numbers to 20

8

Write the number

after 13

after 19

after 17

before 17

before 11

before 20

15

Counting to 20

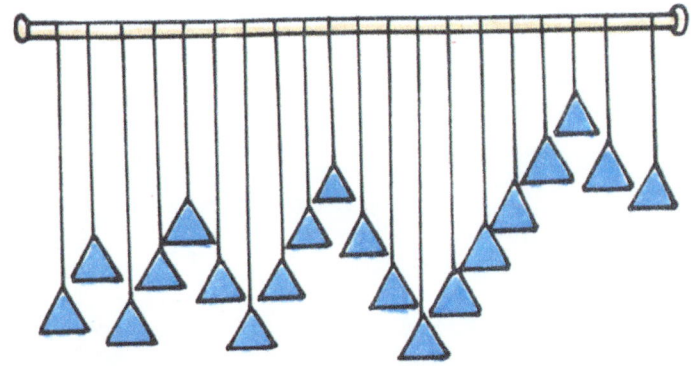

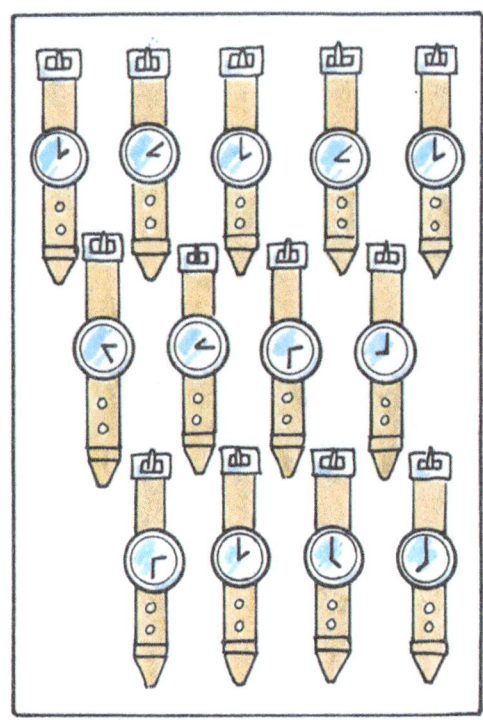

 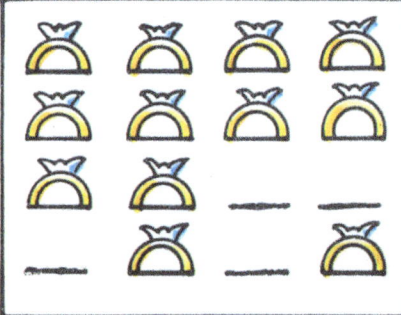 

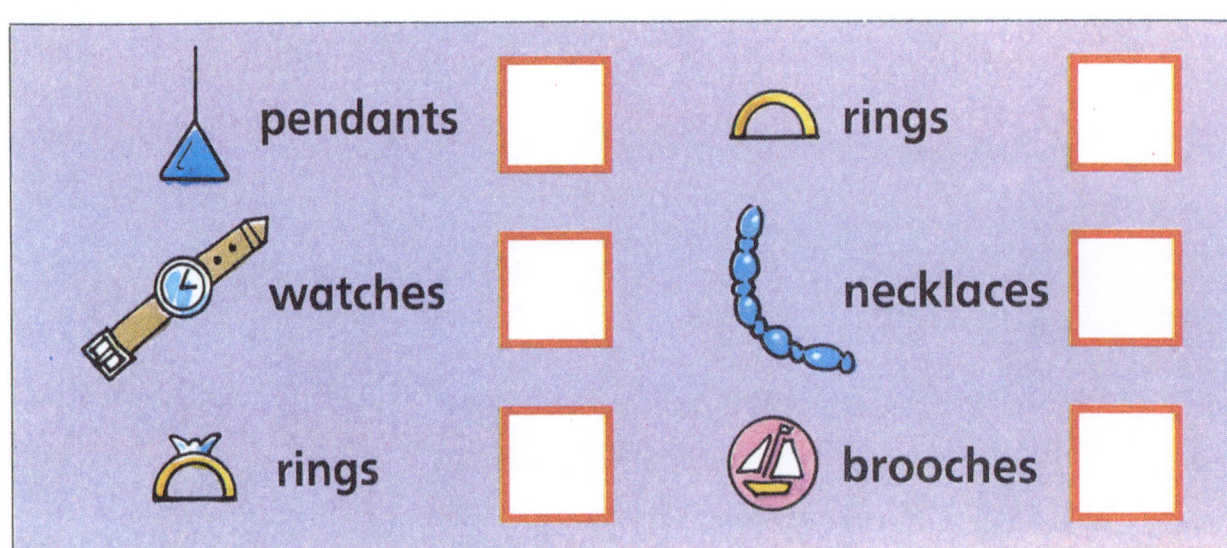

Jewellery shop

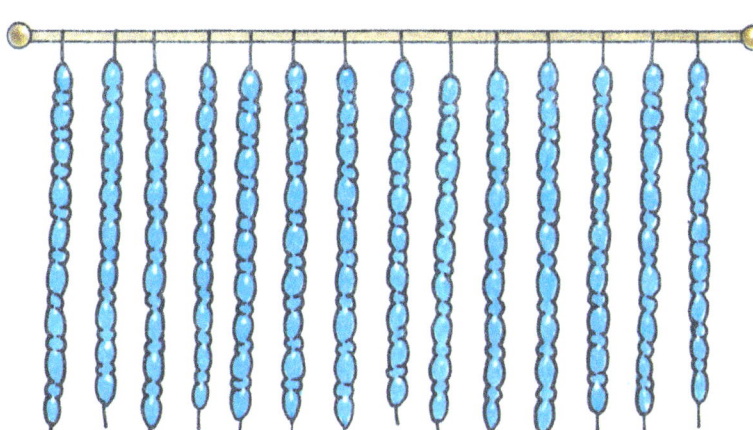
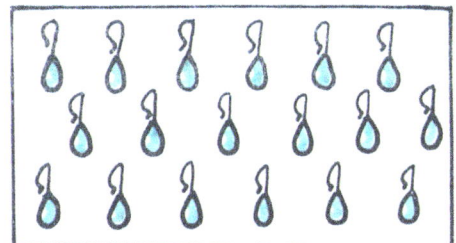
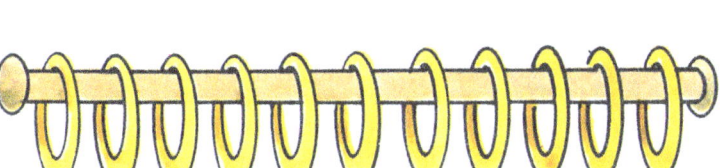

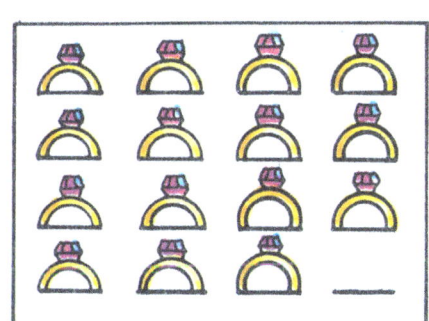
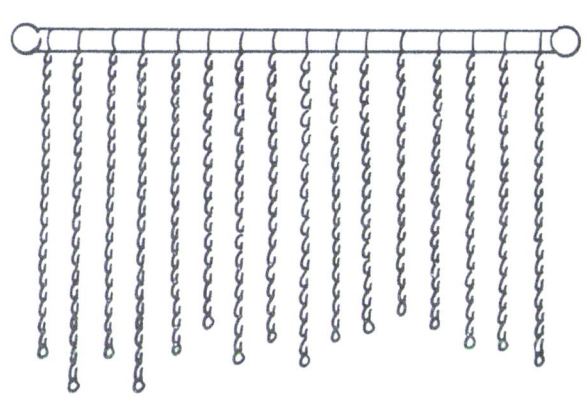

bangles			chains	
rings			rings	
ear-rings			brooches	

Counting to 20

10

Number names to 20

Write the numbers.

Colour twenty red, twelve blue, thirteen yellow and

Use a calculator to show these numbers.
Write the numbers.

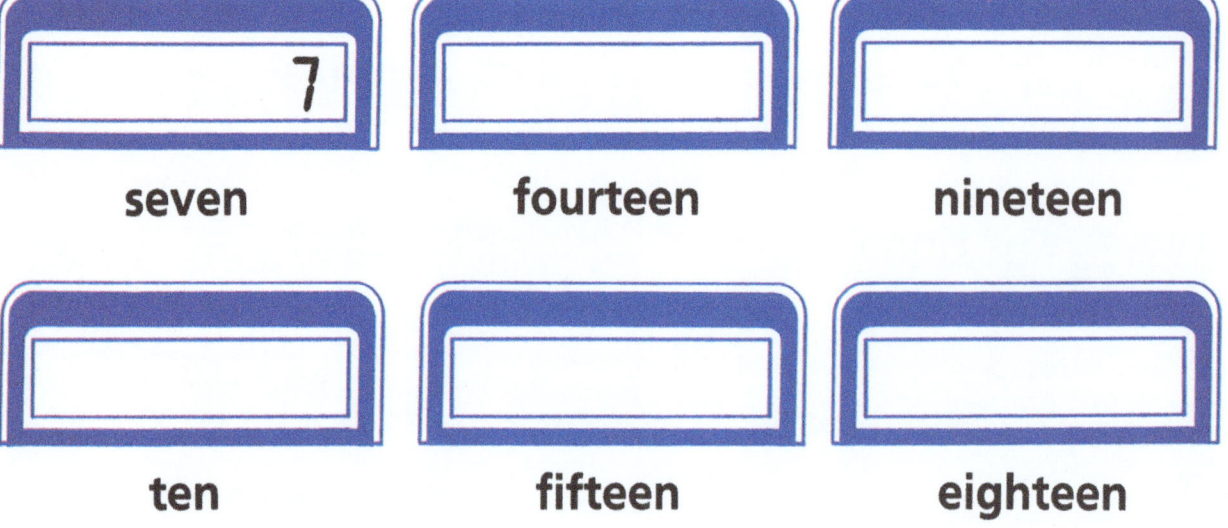

seven   fourteen   nineteen

ten   fifteen   eighteen

names

Number names to 20

12

sixteen | seventeen | eighteen | nineteen | twenty

seventeen green.

Match

nine
eleven
fourteen
sixteen

Towards place value

The sunflower

Use cubes.

Count out 13.
Put 10 on the  .
13 = 10 and 3

Count out 19.
Put 10 on the   .
19 = 10 and ___

Count out 15.
Put 10 on the   .
15 = 10 and ___

Count out 18.
Put 10 on the  .
18 = 10 and ___

Count out 16.
Put 10 on the   .
16 = ___ and ___

Count out 12.
Put 10 on the   .
12 = ___ and ___

The beanstalk

Towards place value — 14

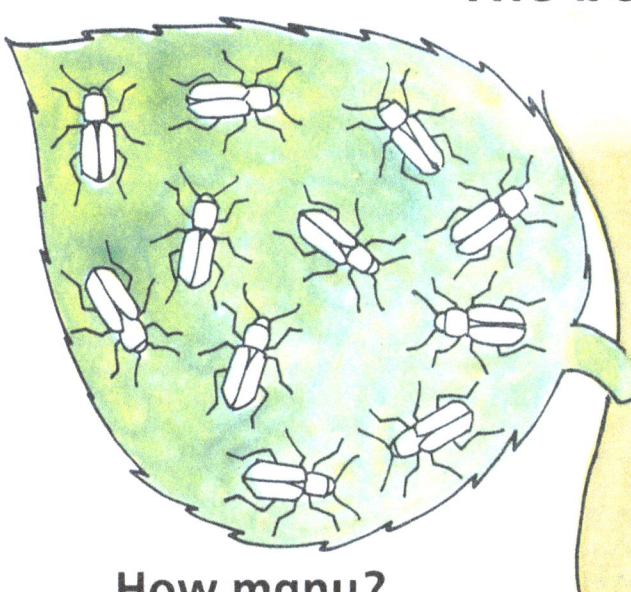

How many? ____
Colour 10 red.

11 = 10 + ____

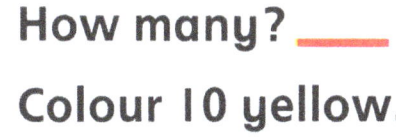

How many? ____
Colour 10 yellow.

14 = 10 + ____

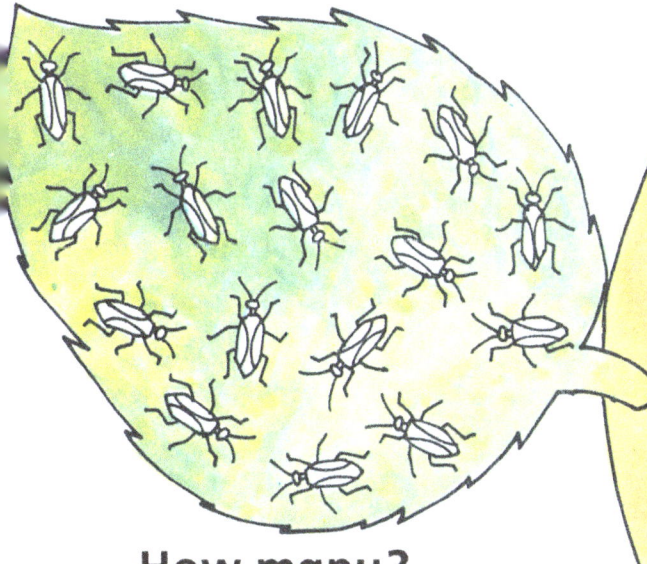

How many? ____
Colour 10 blue.

17 = ____ + ____

How many? ____
Colour 10 purple.

15 = ____ + ____

19 = ____ + ____
12 = ____ + ____
16 = ____ + ____

The garden centre

Loading bricks

Count out 13. Make a ten.

13 = __1__ ten + ____ units

15 = ____ ten + ____ units

18 = ____ ten + ____ units

14 = ____ ten + ____ units

17 = ____ ten + ____ units

19 = ____ ten + ____ units

11 = ____ ten + ____ unit

16 = ____ ten + ____ units

12 = ____ ten + ____ units

20 = ____ tens + ____ units

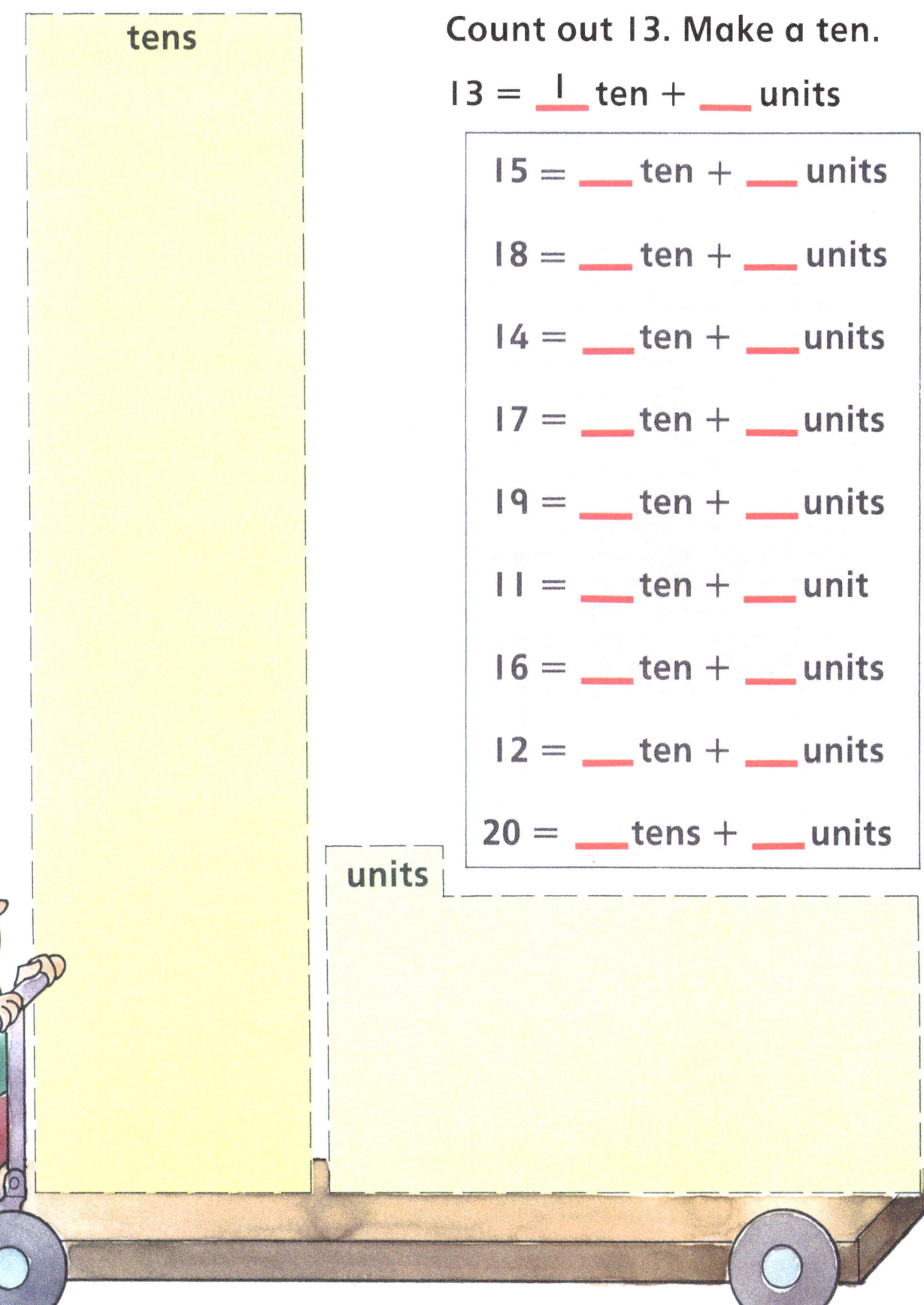

More bricks

tens

units

Put out 1 ten and 5 units.
How many cubes altogether? ☐

1 ten + 5 units = ☐

1 ten + 2 units = ☐

1 ten + 7 units = ☐

1 ten + 4 units = ☐

1 ten + 1 unit = ☐

1 ten + 6 units = ☐

2 tens + 0 units = ☐

Cranes

Colour the boxes to match the cranes.

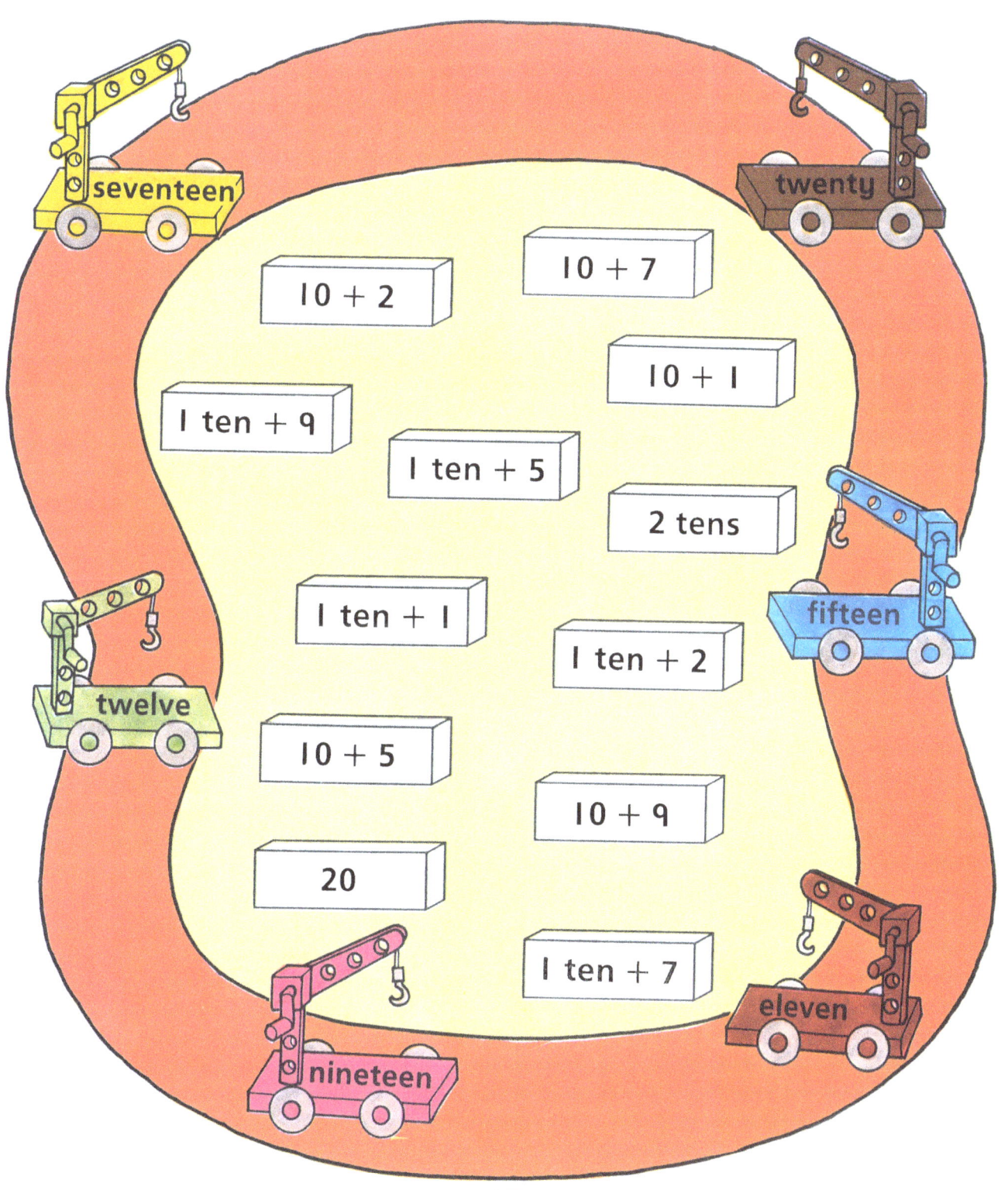

Bunny hops

Start at 4.   Count on 3.   4 + 3 =

Start at 8.   Count on 3.   8 + 3 =

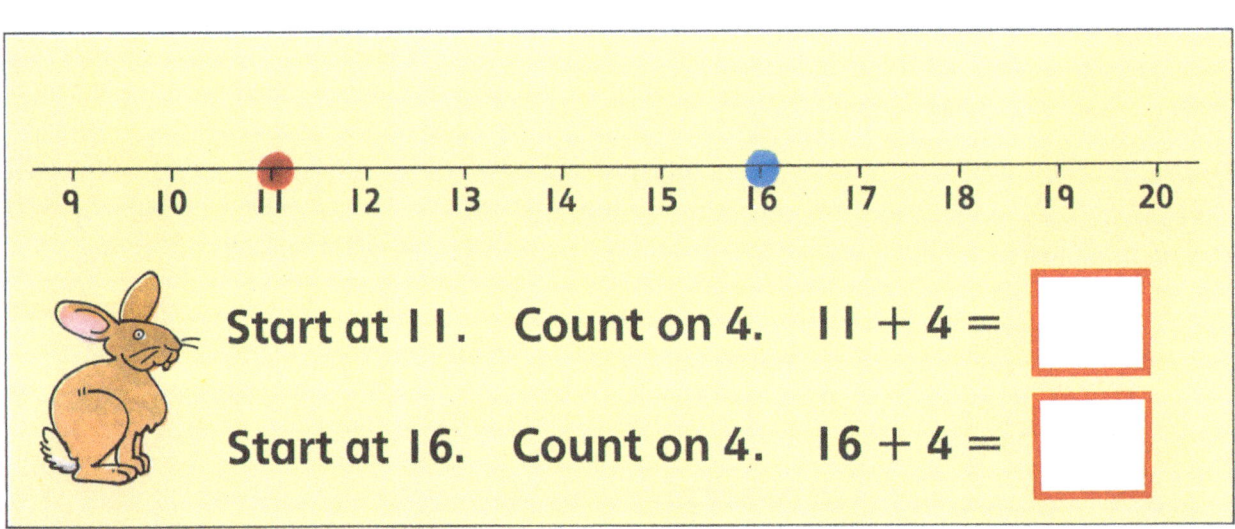

Start at 11.   Count on 4.   11 + 4 =

Start at 16.   Count on 4.   16 + 4 =

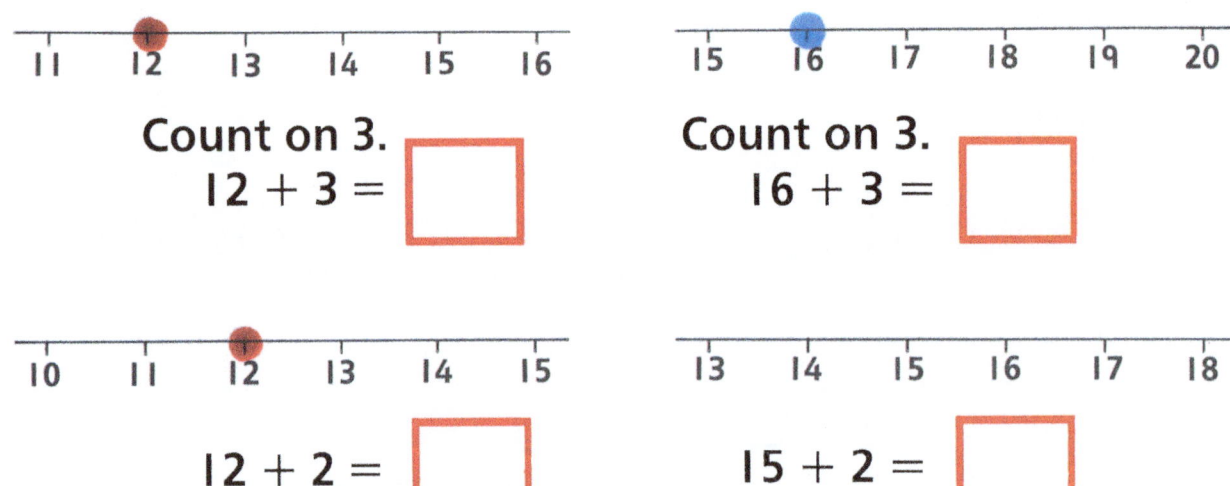

Count on 3.
12 + 3 =

Count on 3.
16 + 3 =

12 + 2 =

15 + 2 =

Party food

Put more cherries on the cake.

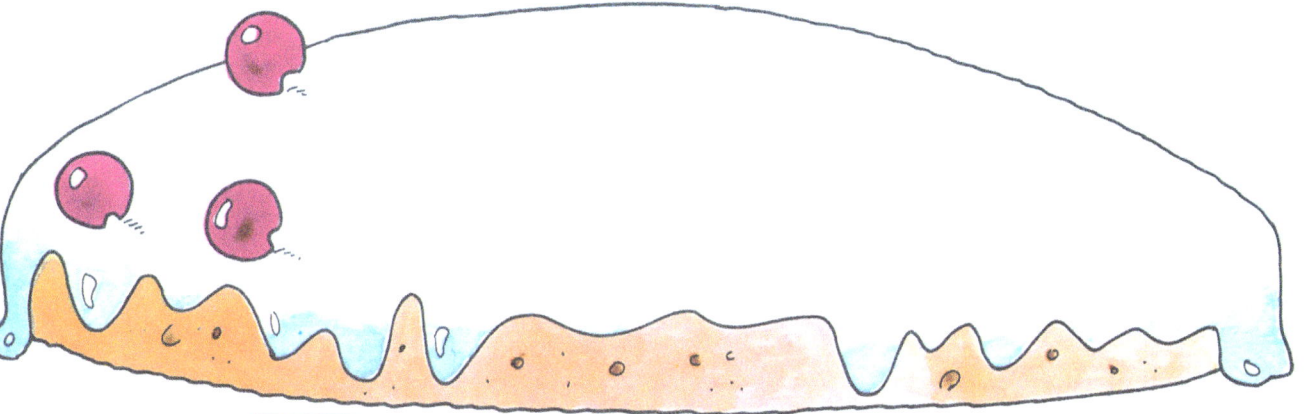

3 + ☐ = 5   3 + ☐ = 4

3 + ☐ = 6   3 + ☐ = 7

3 + ☐ = 9   3 + ☐ = 8

Draw more cakes.   Draw more cakes.

2 + ☐ = 5   5 + ☐ = 8

Draw more apples.   Draw more apples.

   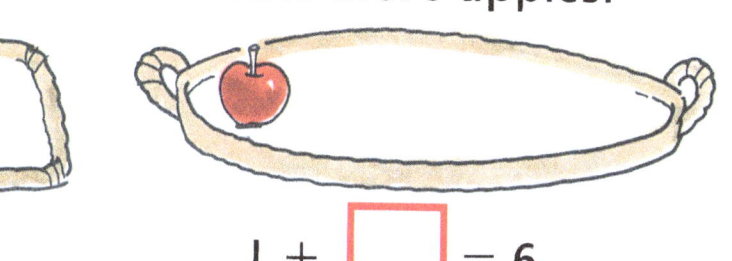

4 + ☐ = 7   1 + ☐ = 6

Complementary addition

21

Boats

Vegetables

Difference in price

22

The difference in price is ☐ p.   6 − 4 =

You may use 🪙 coins.

Difference in price ☐ p   8 − 2 =

Difference in price ☐ p   9 − 6 =

Difference in price ☐ p

Difference in price ☐ p

Difference in price ☐ p

R 10

Plants

☐ plants

☐ plants

The difference between 9 and 6 is ___ .   9 − 6 = ☐

☐ trees

☐ trees

The difference between 4 and 8 is ___ .   8 − 4 = ☐

☐ leaves   ☐ leaves

The difference between 7 and 5 is ___ .

7 − 5 = ☐

The difference between 6 and 3 is ___ .

6 − 3 = ☐

The difference between 2 and 9 is ___ .

9 − 2 = ☐

Money to 9p

2

Match the coins.

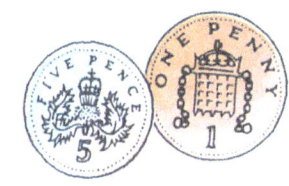
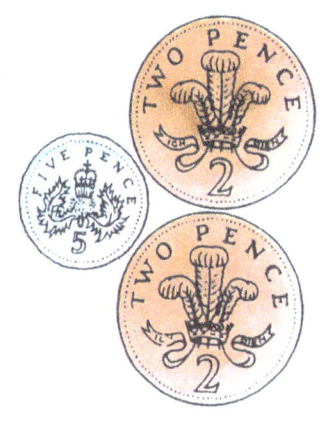

Problem solving

Colour **3** coins to buy a TOFFS.

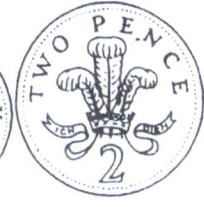

Ten pence

10p coin

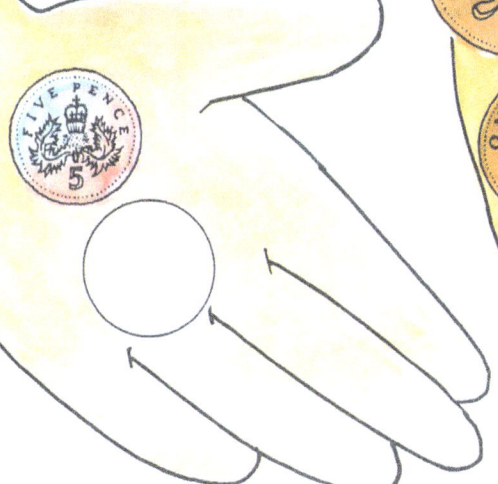

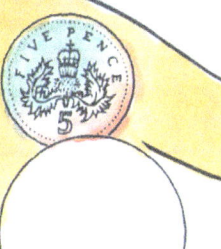

Put out coins. Make each set worth

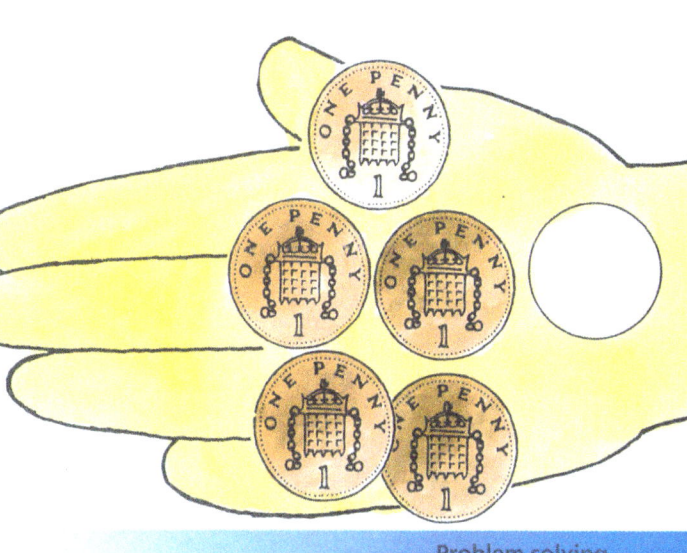

Problem solving

Colour coins to make 10p.

Problem solving

5

Buying things

Tom spends 10p altogether.
Write the price of the boat.

3p   2p

Lili spends 10p.
She buys two things.
Colour their labels.

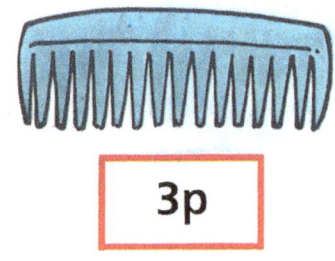

3p

6p

4p

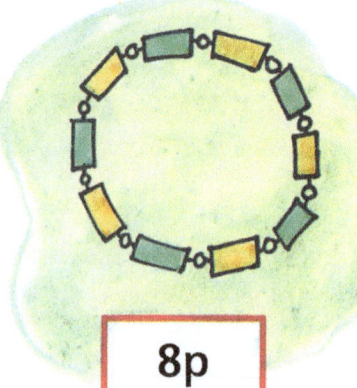

8p

7p

Buying stickers

Use coins. Put out the change.

R 6

2p

Change from 5p

1p

Change from 5p

7p

Change from 10p

4p

Change from 10p

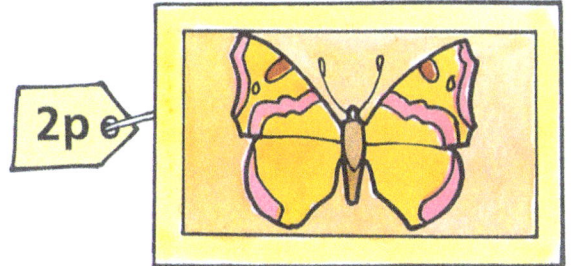

2p

Change from 10p

R 7,8

show

Numbers to 20

8

Write the number

after 13

after 19

after 17

before 17

before 11

before 20

Counting to 20

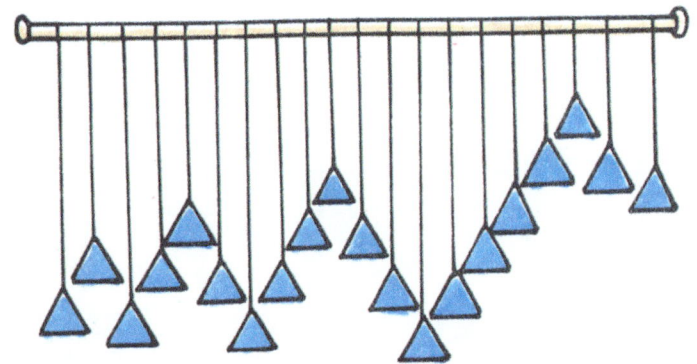

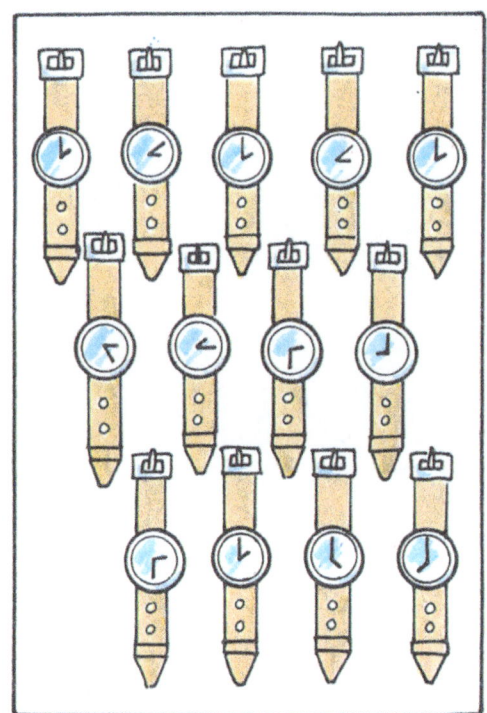

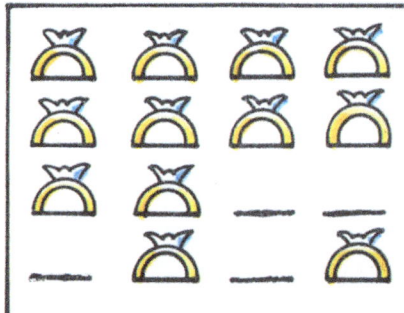

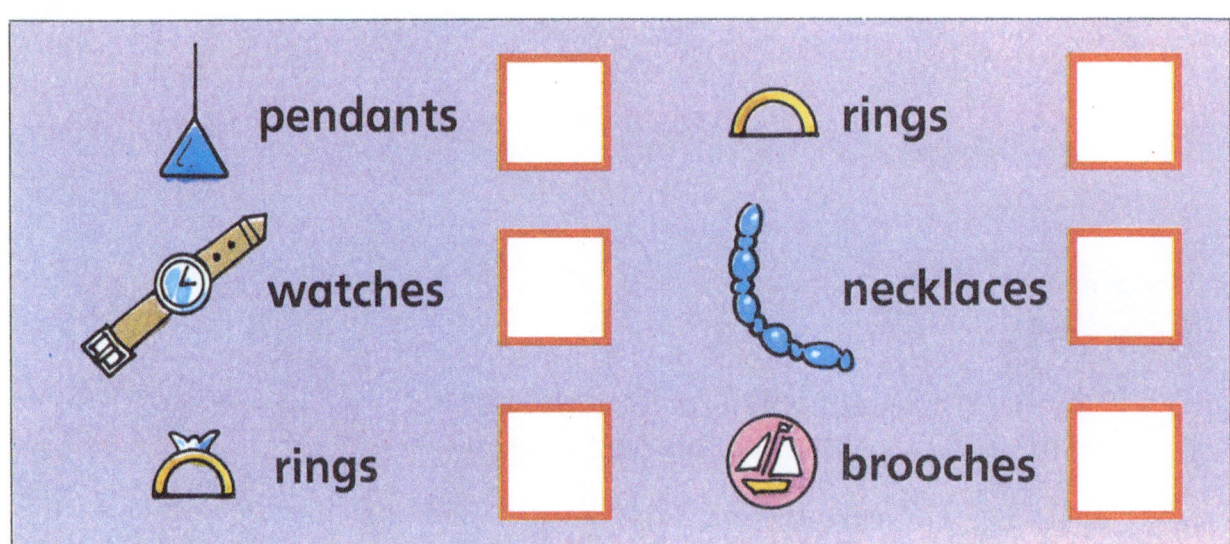

pendants

watches

rings

rings

necklaces

brooches

Jewellery shop

Counting to 20

10

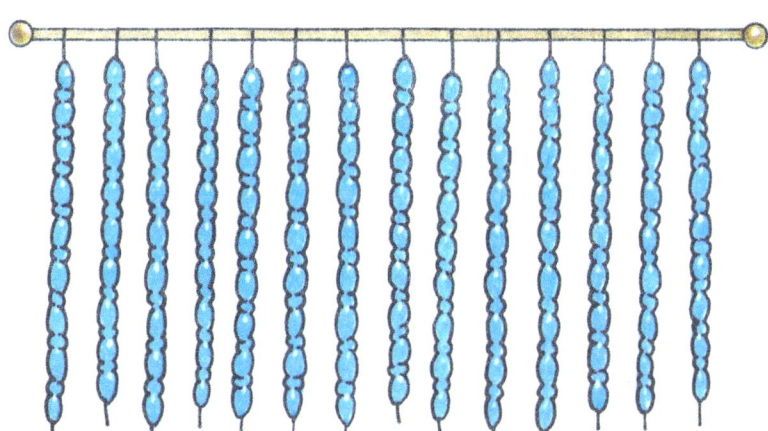
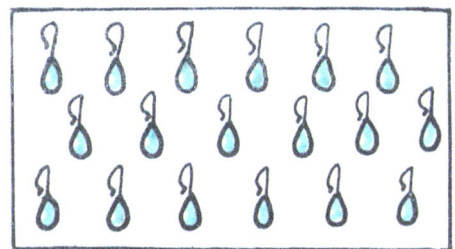
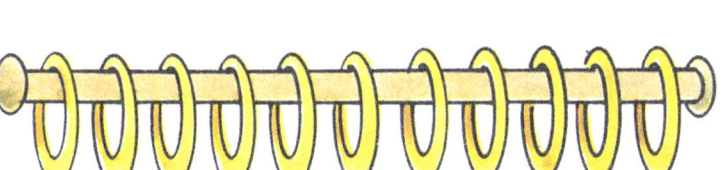
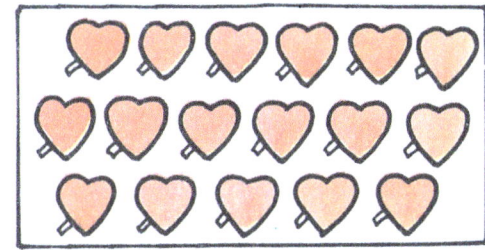

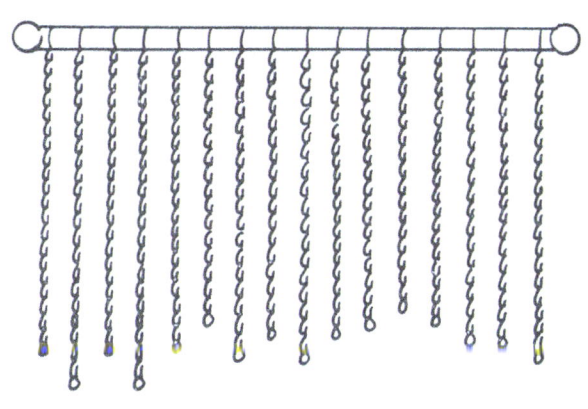
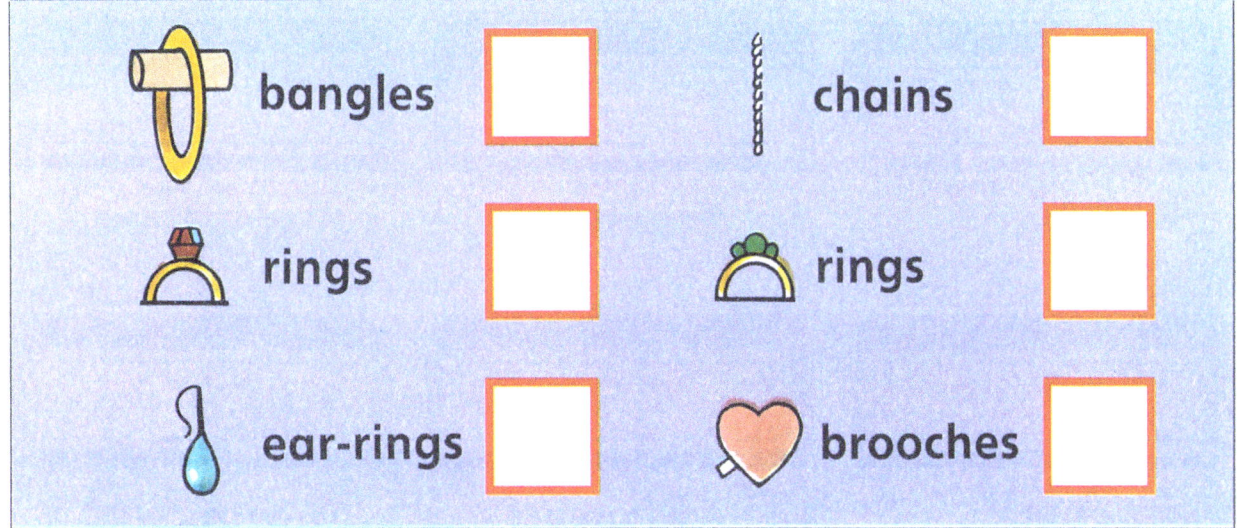

Number names to 20

Write the numbers.

Colour twenty red, twelve blue, thirteen yellow and

Use a calculator to show these numbers.
Write the numbers.

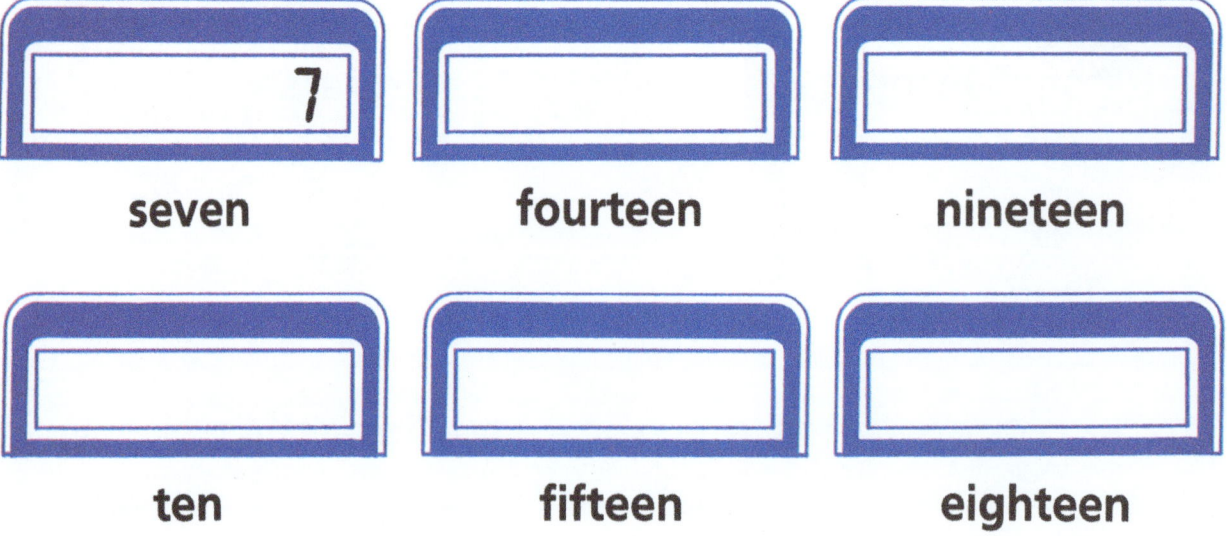

seven   fourteen   nineteen

ten   fifteen   eighteen

names

Number names to 20

16

sixteen   seventeen   eighteen   nineteen   twenty

seventeen green.

The sunflower

Use cubes.

Count out 13.
Put 10 on the  .
13 = 10 and 3

Count out 19.
Put 10 on the   .
19 = 10 and ___

Count out 15.
Put 10 on the   .
15 = 10 and ___

Count out 18.
Put 10 on the  .
18 = 10 and ___

Count out 16.
Put 10 on the   .
16 = ___ and ___

Count out 12.
Put 10 on the   .
12 = ___ and ___

Towards place value

The beanstalk

14

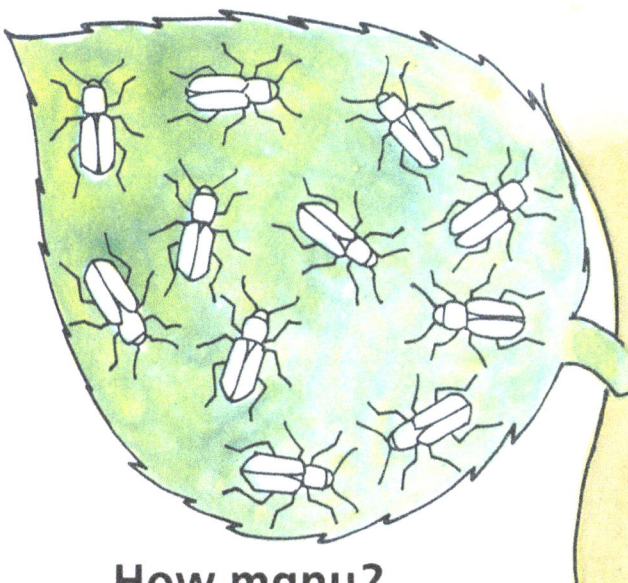

How many? ____
Colour 10 red.

11 = 10 + ____

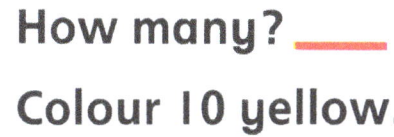

How many? ____
Colour 10 yellow.

14 = 10 + ____

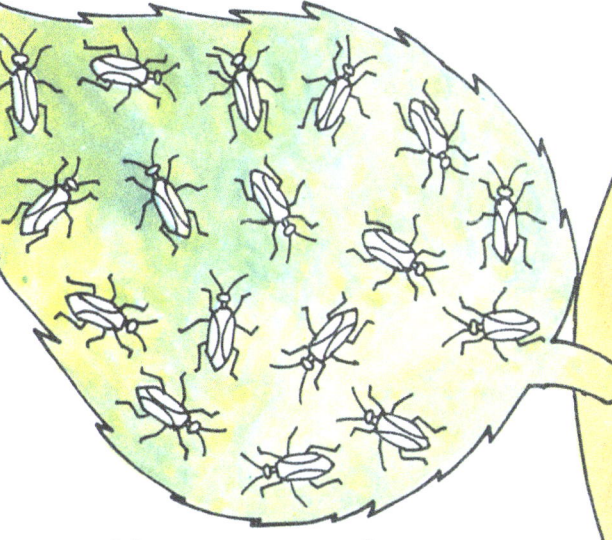

How many? ____
Colour 10 blue.

17 = ____ + ____

How many? ____
Colour 10 purple.

15 = ____ + ____

19 = ____ + ____

12 = ____ + ____

16 = ____ + ____

Towards place value

The garden centre

10 + ___

How many altogether?

10 + ___

How many altogether?

10 + ___

How many altogether?

10 + ___

How many altogether?

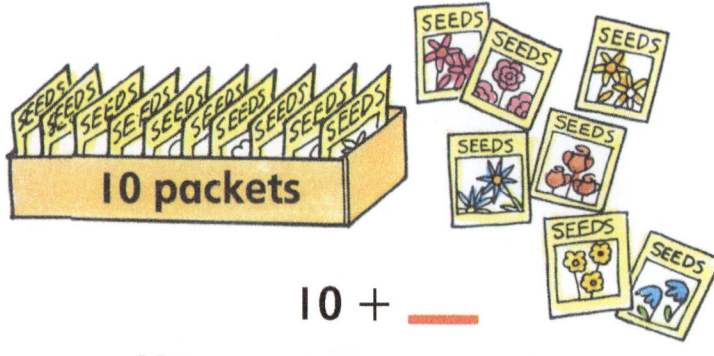

10 + ___

How many altogether?

10 + ___

How many altogether?

Loading bricks

Place value to 20

16

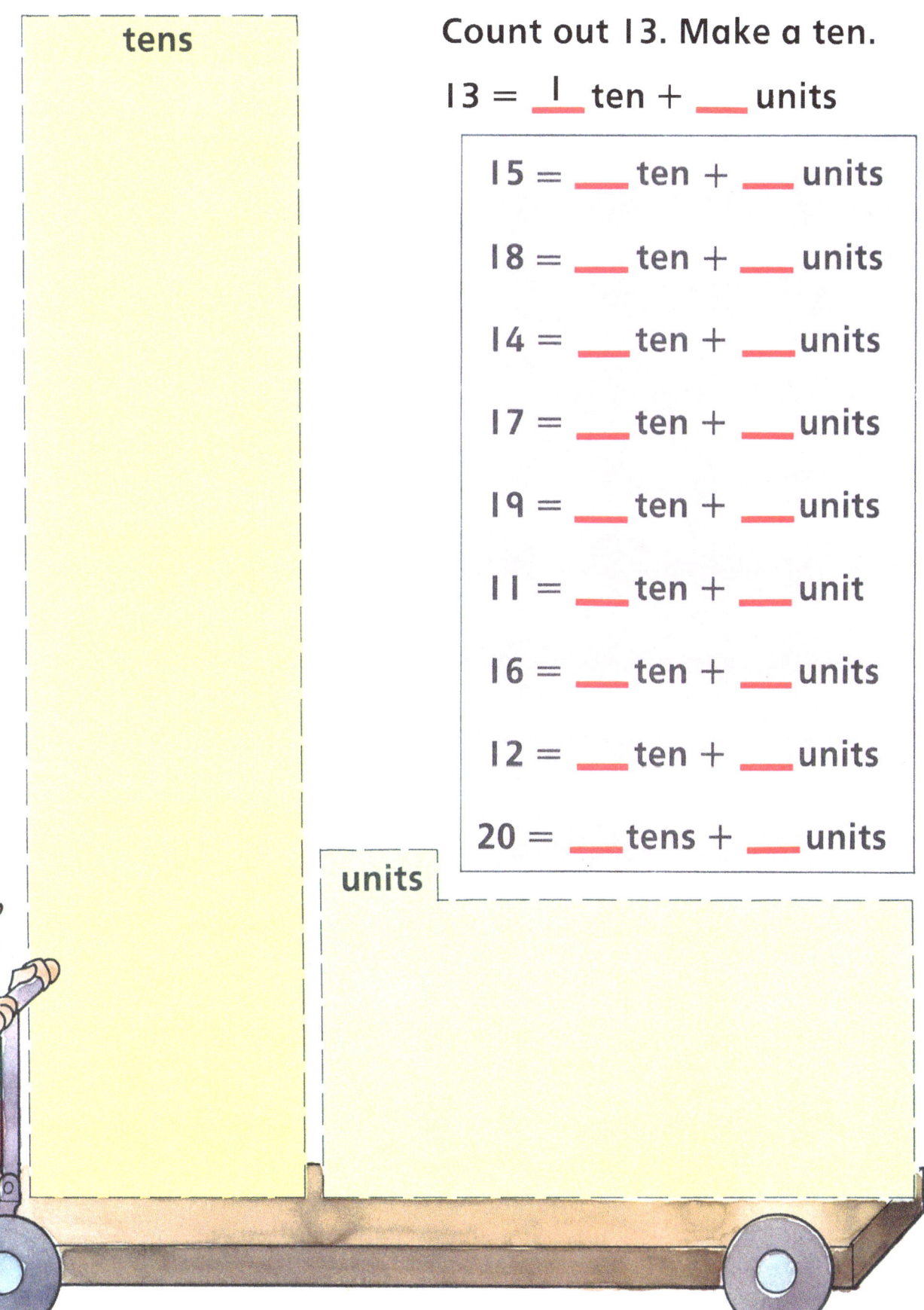

tens

Count out 13. Make a ten.

13 = __1__ ten + ____ units

15 = ____ ten + ____ units

18 = ____ ten + ____ units

14 = ____ ten + ____ units

17 = ____ ten + ____ units

19 = ____ ten + ____ units

11 = ____ ten + ____ unit

16 = ____ ten + ____ units

12 = ____ ten + ____ units

20 = ____ tens + ____ units

units

Place value to 20

More bricks

tens

Put out 1 ten and 5 units.
How many cubes altogether? ☐

1 ten + 5 units = ☐

1 ten + 2 units = ☐

1 ten + 7 units = ☐

1 ten + 4 units = ☐

1 ten + 1 unit = ☐

1 ten + 6 units = ☐

2 tens + 0 units = ☐

units

Cranes

Colour the boxes to match the cranes.

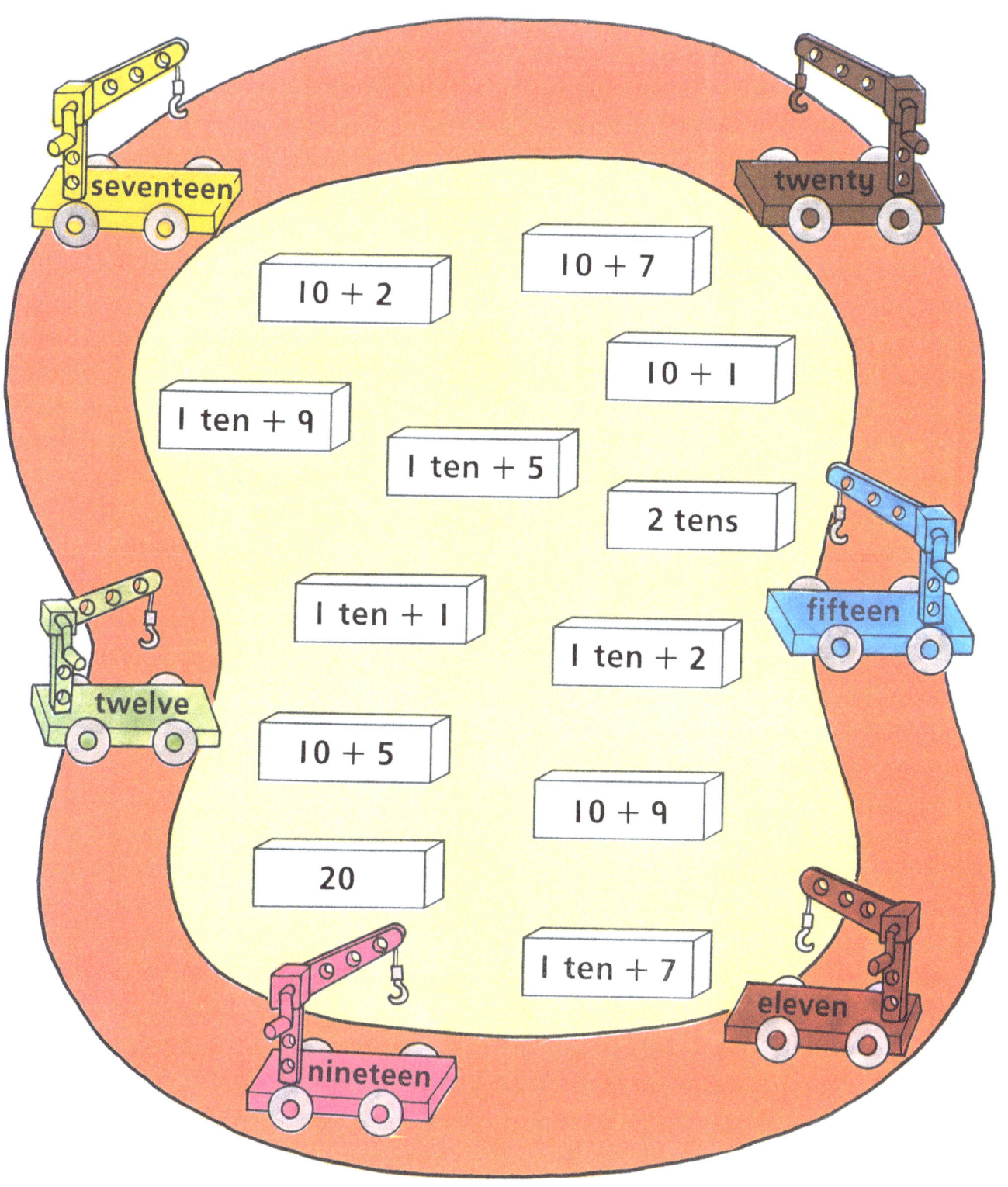

Number line: counting on

Bunny hops

Start at 4.   Count on 3.   4 + 3 = ☐

Start at 8.   Count on 3.   8 + 3 = ☐

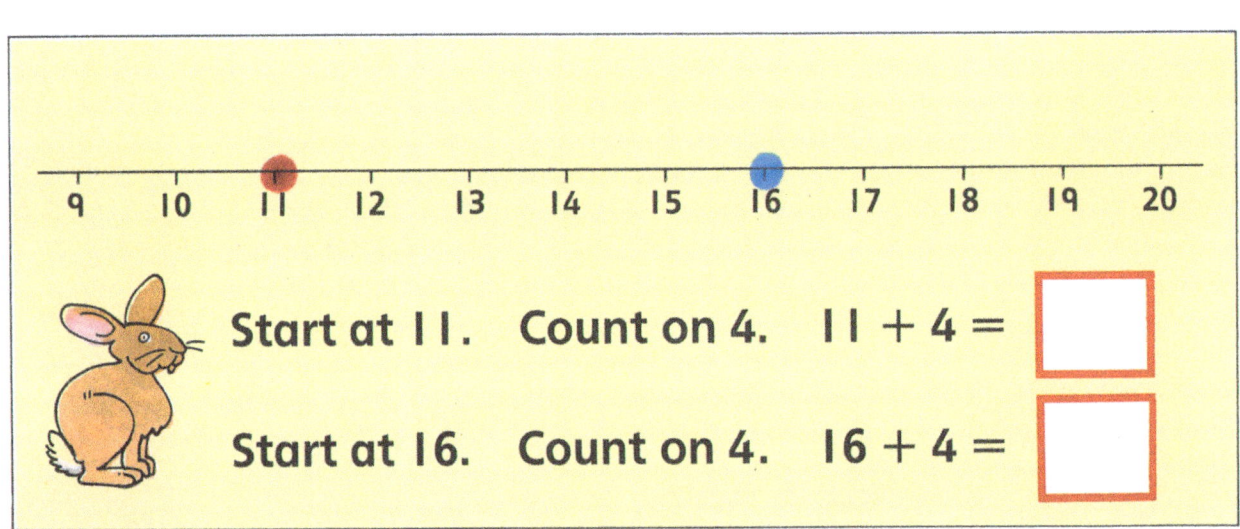

Start at 11.   Count on 4.   11 + 4 = ☐

Start at 16.   Count on 4.   16 + 4 = ☐

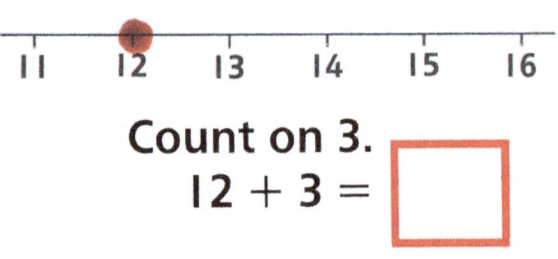

Count on 3.
12 + 3 = ☐

Count on 3.
16 + 3 = ☐

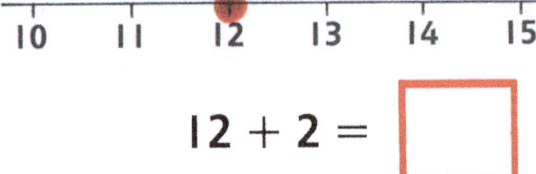

12 + 2 = ☐

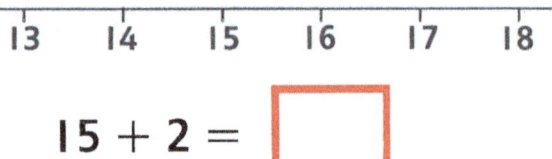

15 + 2 = ☐

Complementary addition

Party food

20

Put more cherries on the cake.

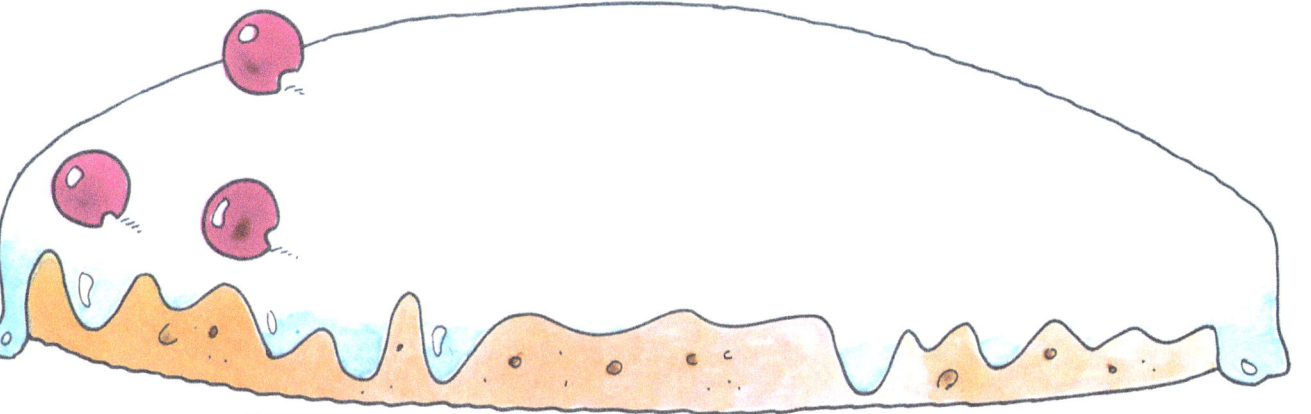

3 + ☐ = 5   3 + ☐ = 4

3 + ☐ = 6   3 + ☐ = 7

3 + ☐ = 9   3 + ☐ = 8

Draw more cakes.   Draw more cakes.

2 + ☐ = 5   5 + ☐ = 8

Draw more apples.   Draw more apples.

   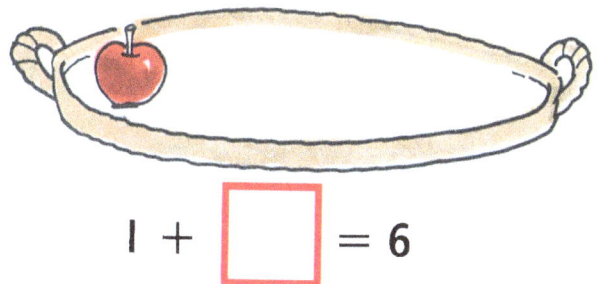

4 + ☐ = 7   1 + ☐ = 6

Complementary addition

Boats

Vegetables

Difference in price

The difference in price is ☐ p.   6 − 4 =

You may use  coins.

  Difference in price ☐ p   8 − 2 =

  Difference in price ☐ p   9 − 6 =

  Difference in price ☐ p

 Difference in price ☐ p

 Difference in price ☐ p

Plants

☐ plants

☐ plants

The difference between 9 and 6 is ___ . 9 − 6 = ☐

☐ trees

☐ trees

The difference between 4 and 8 is ___ . 8 − 4 = ☐

☐ leaves ☐ leaves

The difference between 7 and 5 is ___ .

7 − 5 = ☐

The difference between 6 and 3 is ___ .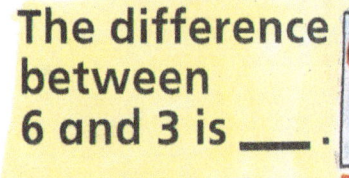

6 − 3 = ☐

 The difference between 2 and 9 is ___ .

9 − 2 = ☐